POETRY COMI

G000160548

GREAT MINDS

Your World...Your Future...YOUR WORDS

From Western Kent

Edited by Heather Killingray

 Young**Writers**

First published in Great Britain in 2005 by:
Young Writers
Remus House
Coltsfoot Drive
Peterborough
PE2 9JX
Telephone: 01733 890066
Website: www.youngwriters.co.uk

SB ISBN 1 84460 709 7

Foreword

This year, the Young Writers' 'Great Minds' competition proudly presents a showcase of the best poetic talent selected from over 40,000 up-and-coming writers nationwide.

Young Writers was established in 1991 to promote the reading and writing of poetry within schools and to the youth of today. Our books nurture and inspire confidence in the ability of young writers and provide a snapshot of poems written in schools and at home by budding poets of the future.

The thought, effort, imagination and hard work put into each poem impressed us all and the task of selecting poems was a difficult but nevertheless enjoyable experience.

We hope you are as pleased as we are with the final selection and that you and your family continue to be entertained with *Great Minds From Western Kent* for many years to come.

Contents

Alex Levey (11) 48
Liam Shipton (11) 49
Hayley Pain (11) 49
David Akinwunmi (11) 50
James Hoang (13) 51
Bart Challis (13) 52
Bonnie-Marie Abhayaratne (13) 53
Josie Charles (11) 54
Lee Dunmore (11) 55
Jack Bates (11) 55
Chris Hughes (13) 56
Srikesh Datta (11) 56
Daniel Akanni (11) 57
Chantelle Datiari (11) 58
Affan Besim (14) 59
Connor Minnican (12) 60
Joey Hosier (11) 60
Seun Olawale (11) 61
Alexandra Smith (11) 61
Julia Smith (11) 62

Cator Park School for Girls

Heather Fitzpatrick (11) 62
Emma Pratt (11) 63
Rachel Carr (12) 63
Sian Randolph (11) 64
Tayla Kelly (11) 65
Anna-Louise Johnson (12) 66
Susanna Jenkins 66
Shenelle Bardall (12) 67
Robyn Burge (12) 67
Chelsea Chandler 68
Janielle Duncan (13) 68
Chelsea Poynter (13) 69
Alexcia Gerald (14) 69
Delphine Lievens (11) 70
Temeka James (13) 70
Latoya Anderson (13) 71
Jamilah Jahi (11) 71
Mithunaa Nuges (11) 72
Rosie Anne Jeffery (13) 72

Rebecca Ashton (12)   73
Emily Sarrah Lahouel (12)   73
Olivia Holland (12)   74
Harriet Rogers (12)   74
Viktorija Lopato (12)   75
Louise Savage (15)   76
Maria Savva (13)   77
Cassandra Gibbs (15)   77
Larissa Barnett (12)   78
Charlotte Speer (13)   79
Jessica Fitch Bunce (12)   80
Jessica Edun (13)   80
Lauren Ellis (12)   81
Charlotte Perkins   81
Jahzmine Vassell (11)   82
Monique Tulloch (13)   83
Caitlin Johnstone (14)   84
Michelle Ashton (13)   85
Acacia Northe (13)   86
Tammika West (14)   87
Hasinae Choudhury (16)   88
Vuyo Kwitshana (14)   89
Jade King (13)   89
Nisa Cooper (14)   90

Hugh Christie Technology College
Michael Parker (11)   90
Madeleine Atkins (12)   91
Luke Chatfield (11)   91
Tom Jones (11)   92
Ben Rowswell (11)   92
Joanne Wilson (11)   93
Jasmine Thomson (11)   93
Georgia Van Ebeling (11)   94
Kayleigh Williamson (11)   94
Abbie White (12)   95
Sophie Littlechild (11)   95
Shannon Jenkins (12)   96
Kenny Martin (11)   96
Zoë Everest (11)   97
Rosie Try (11)   97

Peter Kilpatrick (11)	98
Daniel Finn (11)	98
Holly James (12)	99
Zoë Pennells (11)	99
Keighley Kucers (11)	100
Sam Hasler (11)	100
Jemma Dunville (11)	101
Grant Stonehouse (11)	101
Matthew J Smith (12)	102
Jake Fairweather (11)	102
Thomas Prior (11)	103
Cortney Osborne (11)	103
Max Maton (11)	104
Rebecca Broad (11)	104
Ben Turner (11)	105
Emily Hazell (11)	105
Zoe Chatfield (11)	106
Hayley Tompson (11)	106
Katie Harris (11)	107
Joannah Roots (11)	107
Natalie Gillham (11)	108
Danielle Standen (12)	108
Alexander Hughesman (11)	109
Jackson Harris (12)	109
Ben Payne (11)	109
Chloé Shrubsole (12)	110
Liam Foster (12)	110
Emily Charman (12)	111
Stephen Connor (11)	111
Ben James (11)	112
Luke Powell (12)	112
Sam Chesson (11)	113
Brett Wallis (11)	113
Emma Broom (11)	114
Joshua Dalby (11)	114
Tommy Smith (11)	115
Perry Smith (11)	115
Michael Fox (11)	116
Reece Huggins (12)	116
Alex Richardson (11)	117
Liam Palmer (12)	117
Lauren Claire Gillham (11)	117

Langley Park School for Boys

Bevan Freake (13)   139
Adam Smith (13)   139
Nick Clegg (13)   140
Edwin Evelyn-Rahr (13)   141
Joe Jefford (12)   142
Harry Birch (13)   142
George Haylett (12)   143
Rob Horgan (13)   144
Dominic Oliver (12)   144
Joshua Crowhurst (12)   145
Shanil Chande (13)   145
Stephen Carter (12)   146
Ashley Wiles (13)   147
Edward Stone (13)   148
Tom Williams (13)   149
Stephen Roche (13)   150

Marjorie McClure School

Antonia Martinez (11)   150
Ethan Middleton (14)   151
Katie Mott (11)   151
Fozia Sarfraz (14)   152
Christian Bush (14)   152
Mark Seagers (14)   153
Josie Keeler (13)   153
Foday Turay (13)   154
Jack Cox (14)   154
Craig Wilson (11)   154
Nicki Harper (15)   155
Kristian Heath (11)   155
Aphra Kenny-Mastihi (12)   156
Sarah Dowding (11)   156
Oliver Murray-Brown (13)   157
Thomas Clements (15)   157
Paul Poulton (15)   157
Simon Robinson (14)   158
Marie Murray (11)   158
Sarah Webb (16)   159
Lauren Hendricks (11)   159
Jordan Findlay (12)   159
Kimberley O'Connor (13)   160

Parkwood Hall School

The Grammar School for Girls, Wilmington

The Poems

Lady Ashbrook's Ball

As the people flowed
The lights glistened forever
They laughed and they groaned
As if they were called Trevor

We've got live comedians
From Peter Kay to Harry Hill
Performing with a chameleon
And we might even ring the Bill

As the balloons pop
And the Christmas tree sparkles
The jugglers hop
While lords and ladies bop

As the wine flows
The children dance together
The waiters do their waiting
Like it will go on forever and ever.

Archie Woodgate (11)
Bexley Grammar School

The Enchanted Forest

It's dark and shadowy out here in the night.
The eeriness gives me a fright.
The only light is provided by the fairies' glow.
There are elves everywhere, are they friend or foe?
The trees are howling in their sleep
The baby imps are playing hide don't peep.
The unicorns are flying close to the moon
I'm lost and I need to go home soon.

Heather Louise Thorn (11)
Bexley Grammar School

Party Poem

At my party we are rich,
We do not take to the sick.
Gleaming pillars everywhere,
Different costumes bring the fear.

At my party the food's delicious,
We only serve things that are suspicious.
Spider gauderies green as grass,
Honey-glazed bananas gold as brass.

At my party there's so much fun,
Be very aware it's just begun.
Games of various varieties,
Games like 'Kiss Aphrodite'.

At my party the fun has ended,
Time to say bye to those I've befriended
Turn out the lights and do it with plight,
So that there will be a peaceful night.

Oyin Ebikeme (11)
Bexley Grammar School

Plankton

Darting in and out of the tattered seaweed,
Moving in large groups, following the leader.
A desperate struggle to stay alive every day,
Swimming, hiding - desperate to get away.
Trying to escape the biggest fish in the sea,
Small enough to get caught with the waves.
Moving from place to place just trying to stay alive.
Eating small insects: breakfast, lunch and dinner,
Sleeping with one eye open always being cautious.
At last the fish has got away,
The plankton lives to see another day.

Robert McDonald (13)
Bexley Grammar School

Girls' Night In

A girl's in her teens
Just hit thirteen
A gaggle of giggly girls
Come onto the party scene.

Spin the bottle, what will you bare
A measly truth or an embarrassing dare?
Girly movie, laughs I'll bet
Shop till you drop, just wait yet!

Pizza galore
Chips in store
Frothy cappuccinos, taste great
Then the gorgeous cake, brought in on a plate.

Time to go home, in the early morning
They've just gone to sleep, got up and yawning
Mum and Dad relieved, none of this for another year
Dad'll sit down, tired, and drink a beer.

Laura Elvin (11)
Bexley Grammar School

My Dog Jed

I have a dog named Jed,
He has ears too big for his head.
He scoots round the garden all day long,
I know him so well, it's easy to write this song.
If he was a person we would always have a chatter,
But he is not, so he just eats and gets fatter and fatter.
He is definitely my best mate,
Mainly because I have had him since I was eight, he is so great.
There is nothing in the world that I would change Jed for,
Not even for a house on the seashore!

Harvey Lee (12)
Bexley Grammar School

My Hallowe'en Party

A Hallowe'en party,
It's fancy dress,
No need to look tarty,
Just look your best.

Try the food,
It tastes very nice,
Don't be so rude,
Only one slice!

There's lots of fun and games,
The rules are simple,
Like jumping over flames,
Or pop the pimple.

If you want to come to my party,
You better beware,
Unless you have nerves of steel,
You're in for a scare!

Charlie Britland (12)
Bexley Grammar School

My Little Duck

I see ducks everywhere,
Quack, quack, quack as I glare.
But my little duck is especially fond,
Of her little house by the pond.
All she does is swim and eat,
Then dances to her favourite beat.
Worms and slugs and bits of bread,
No wonder she is so well fed.
Her tiny webbed feet and her cute little beak,
There's no question why her feathers are so sleek.
When my duck eats or drinks,
She must get 40 winks,
To get up early in the morning.

Naomi Keerthiratna (13)
Bexley Grammar School

Birthday Party

'Welcome to my birthday party,
Food and fun and games galore.
Thank you for the lovely present,
Come inside and shut the door.'

Everyone's here in fancy dress,
Pirates, monsters fill the room.
Six princesses, sparkly dresses.
Witches riding on their brooms.

Crunchy, fantastic, salty crisps,
Chips a golden light brown.
Snacks delicious, jelly wobbly,
'Bring more food, it's running down!'

Birthday cake with thirteen candles.
'Coke or Tango in your cup?
Now my party's nearly over,
It's time to help me tidy up!'

Peter Long (11)
Bexley Grammar School

Root The Polar Bear And His Rather Annoying Coat

The polar bear, the polar bear,
He has a handsome coat to wear.

But while it's thick and warm and white,
He has to wear it day and night.

And when the summer comes, poor Root,
He wears it for his swimming suit.

'It's just not fair!' says little Root,
'I'd rather not look so cute.

Although his coat does look so fine,
I'm very glad that it's not mine.'

Vicky Marchant (12)
Bexley Grammar School

Party

I'm having a party, it's going to be fun,
I think I have invited almost everyone.
We're going to have games and stuff like that,
And I'll be wearing a witch's hat.

We will have apple bobbing and a witch's brew game,
And all that stuff, it's all the same.
We will also have a mime,
Who will be dressed up as Dracula or Frankenstein.

We're going to have a competition on who is the best person
in fancy dress,
I hope that I come first or I will get distressed.
We had the fancy dress results and I came 4th or 3rd
But the person who came first was dressed as a bird.

Now everyone is drunk and lying on the floor,
I don't think they will want beer any more.
Everyone's at home now but they all had fun,
I think I'll call them up again and arrange another one.

Siân Williams (11)
Bexley Grammar School

Owls

I see it now,
A rapid flying animal, its wings stop and start,
Stop and start as the weak breeze makes the tree
Slowly rustle in the cool night.

Then suddenly I hear a very annoying screeching sound;
It's coming from behind me.
I turn, there it is.
A large, fur-coated bird like animal eating away at its prey.
Is it a bird? Is it a plane?
No! It's an owl.

So to wake the owl is an atrocity,
It wants peace alone in its tree.

Tayler Mott (12)
Bexley Grammar School

The Party At Ashbrook House

Melissa was wearing a pretty dress,
Alexander couldn't help but stare,
A weird teen arrived whose head was a mess,
With his killing father who didn't care.

Alexander and Melissa kissed,
The weird teen gazed at them and screamed,
He ran into the forest, into the mist,
Melissa's blue eyes gleamed.

Melissa and her 'boyfriend' went into the main room,
Where they found the guests having great time,
She went onto the dance floor with her maybe future groom,
But then she tripped on some old food and was covered in grime.

Melissa went to clean her messy gown,
So Alexander was single and looking,
The guests carried on boogying down,
But then the cook started her amazing cooking.

There was crispy chicken and tender roast beef,
Pork and vegetables and delicious rabbit stew,
But then oh my! Good heavens! Good grief!
There were so many hungry people they had to form a queue.

Alexander's girlfriend finally came back down clean,
The guests started to leave and they all said the party was great,
Some were drunk and started to act all hard and mean,
The children all went up to bed because the party ended very late.

Ellie Healy (11)
Bexley Grammar School

Birthday Party

We have invited all the guests
This party is going to be the best
We seem to have invited loads
Everyone is wearing their party clothes.

There are lots of little cakes
All week we have done nothing but bake
The amount of food we have is barmy
We have enough to feed an army.

We have hired a huge hall
But with all the guests, it seems small
Someone has sprayed lots of silly string
The loud music is making my ears ring.

Everyone is having lots of fun
I wonder whose dancing will be number one
For the karaoke everyone is singing
But they are all rubbish so no one is winning.

Now everyone has gone home
And I'm off to bed.

Jessica Mathers (11)
Bexley Grammar School

The Time Of Midnight

Clasping, moaning trees scratching at the Earth's floor,
Silver, glistening light shining from above.
Yellow, non-blinking eyes forever watching you,
Wherever you go.
Glistening stars twinkling,
Forever going in the night sky.

The rustle of a still tree,
The cry from a nearby beast.

This is the time of mystery.
This is the time of midnight!

Jessica Louise Luton (12)
Bexley Grammar School

The Ball

The guests all went
to the ball,
They entered by the
door at the wall.

The decorations inside
were tremendous,
Outside was just
as stupendous.

The food was
really, really good,
For the cooks did
the best that they could.

They even had a
giant chocolate cake,
That only the world's best
cook could make.

The entertainment
was great,
It will keep you awake
till late.

The mime had
really long hair,
He looked like a
big grizzly bear.

Towards the end
of the ball,
The waitress
did fall . . .
and spilt cake all over a guest!

Emma Baldwin (11)
Bexley Grammar School

Christmas Party

There's lots of decorations
Red, white and green
There's a big celebration
It's a happy scene.

The beautiful cake
Which has impressed
Took ages to bake
What a success.

The room is full of Christmas lights
Everyone is singing
This is the happiest of nights
The party is really swinging.

The party's over, time for goodbye
It's been a night full of cheer
Now we hope, time will fly
Till we do it again next year.

Rachel Eliza Shackleton (11)
Bexley Grammar School

Winter

As the season of winter draws on,
the nights become dark and cold.

Everybody in their hats and scarves,
with glowing cheeks and numb fingers.

Stars lighting up the black skies,
illuminating the grim city streets.

Animals gathering provisions for
the long, lonely nights ahead.

Winter, the season with a special birth,
of Jesus Christ in the stable.

Nicole De-Menezes (13)
Bexley Grammar School

Party Poem

Everyone drooling all over the food
And people drinking their favourite booze
Some of the world's most brilliant cakes
Although they are quite easy to make

Loads of guests from wall to wall
Some of them big and some of them small
A selection of clothes, some of the posh
You can tell that these people have lots of dosh

And right at the top of the hall
Is the grand disco ball
Colourful decorations everywhere
All of the children stop to stare

Everyone dancing to the songs
Some of them short and some of them long
The magical magician amazes and shocks
And flying in the air is the cork.

Adam Riza (11)
Bexley Grammar School

I Wish . . .

I wish I was a pink flamingo fishing in the mangroves of America.
I wish I was a great white shark swiftly searching
and sharply moving through the sea.
I wish I was a ginger cat silently stalking its cowering prey
in a still, lamplit street.
I wish I was a giant grey elephant lazing in the blazing,
golden sun of Africa.
I wish I was a lime green tree boa winding its way
through twisted, spindly branches.
I wish I was a fiery orange and jet-black tiger
padding softly through the jungle.

Lauren Exford (11)
Bexley Grammar School

The Party

There are lots of clowns
All ready to make you laugh
With lots of sounds
But not there to make you barf

Here comes Mr Claymore
He is very posh
He comes with Roger Moore
Who wants lots of dosh

Our cook is Mr Lovejoy
But not our baker
No cakes for girls and boys
He goes swimming in a lake

Remember the decorations
Already for Hallowe'en
The children are on an exploration
But the Devil is nowhere to be seen.

Myles Benford (11)
Bexley Grammar School

The Forest

In the forest of the night,
The stars were shining and sparkling bright.

The tall trees stood still,
And the animal noises made you thrill.

Up in the sky 'twas the light from the moon,
And all you could hear was the peaceful tune.

From the animals asleep and the stars above,
All you could see was the running of love.

Nicola Beeson (11)
Bexley Grammar School

The Party

As the party began
There was jokes all around
It was really great fun
And there was a headaching sound

We've got live comedians
From Peter Kay to Harry Hill
We've also got pet chameleons
And the actors' jokes kill

We've got a live DJ with disco lights
And a 10ft deluxe cake
So far there's been 57 fights
And the cake is vanilla shake

As the party was ending
There were loads of men drunk
But there was still people attending
And all the men smelt like skunk.

Liam Noctor (11)
Bexley Grammar School

The Enchanted Night

'Twas midnight and all was well,
Until one heard an awful bell.
And when it rang, it woke the trees,
It woke the birds, it woke the bees.
From then on nothing would sleep,
And the creatures, they would weep and weep.
In the woods all was silent,
Until the trees turned very violent.
They lashed out, oh how they howled!
The trees, they grumbled, screeched and growled.
It turned into a dreadful night,
Anyone would get a fright.

Beth Thomas (11)
Bexley Grammar School

Party Poem

The ballroom was looking very great,
With sparkling chandeliers,
There was lots of food on the plate,
Including succulent deer.

There was a very silly man,
To entertain the crowd,
He had a very funny plan,
The laughs were really loud.

My special guests were very happy,
With heaps of fun and jokes,
The DJ's music was very snappy,
Up dancing were the women and blokes.

My party was for everyone,
The men drunk all the beer,
Full of laughter and lots of fun,
You really should've been here.

Sam James (11)
Bexley Grammar School

Winter

She drapes her white cloak across the Earth at
different times.

Her wardrobe flies away and only comes back in spring
or even summer.

As people break her smooth, white carpet by crunching
and stamping
She cries white tears - they fall and fall.

Then she tries her hardest to beat the glorious sun,
but she is defeated!

Somehow I feel she's coming back next year!

Amy Fisher (11)
Bexley Grammar School

The Party

The whole world and his wife came to the ball,
When they first arrived they thought it was cool,
Women dressed from head to toe in red, gold and pink,
They must have spent thousands . . . I think.

Profiteroles piled mountain high with chocolate sauce,
They were having tender roast chicken for their main course,
With thousands of drinks all stacked together,
Everyone's outside because of the lovely weather.

The entertainment was great,
The DJ playing alongside his mate,
With clowns jumping from here to there,
You wouldn't believe they were everywhere.

Hanging from the ceiling were shining disco balls,
Reflecting their patterns onto the walls,
Tinsel swinging from the ceiling in pink, red and white,
The party went on . . . long into the night.

Charlotte Locke (11)
Bexley Grammar School

The Weather Poem

The luminous orange rays of the sun
glimmer over the whole world.
Rain, it pours, cold and icy drops of water.
The sun's enemy lurks in the wet cold nights of winter.
Droplets of snow clatter to the floor,
waiting to melt when the sun comes out.
Clouds gather in the grey dark air,
thunder strikes in thick yellow forks through the air.
Only for rain again.

Josh Thompson (11)
Bexley Grammar School

A Bloke Party

I went to this party,
Which was a laugh and a joke.
You should've been there,
But it was only for blokes.

There was Peter Kay,
And The Darkness too.
The entertainment went on all day,
It was definitely for you.

There was an 'all you can eat' buffet,
Like succulent deer.
This party was in May,
When we drunk all the beer.

You would've loved the live DJ,
Who played all day.
You would've danced all night,
Until it was light.

I wish you were there,
Cos it was a laugh and a joke.
But I'm sorry my friend,
You're not a bloke.

Michael Heming (11)
Bexley Grammar School

My Hallowe'en Party

As I put up my party decorations,
I dance to the song,
I'm in the mood for a celebration,
The guests won't be long!

Ding! Dong! That's them, they're here,
I chase to the door,
They're scary I fear,
And look . . . there's more!

The games begin,
Apple bobbing is first,
I really want to win,
But I must be cursed!

There are big grey bats,
And wicked witches,
Little black cats,
And my costume itches!

The party came to an end,
Everyone went separate ways,
I love to be with my friends,
And maybe I will be again some day.

Rachel Wilson (12)
Bexley Grammar School

Party Poem

The nightclub sounds fill the air
Party goers flock to their lair
The disco ball destroys the dark
Through shining lights and glittering sparks

The alcohol is everywhere
A sober man; incredibly rare
The till is full, the beer is flowing
What happens outside, no one knowing

No clubbers sitting, all on their feet
Dancing to the nightclub beat
All jumping up in wild excite
Never stop, dance through the night

The dance dies down
The music's drowned
And for once
The club is empty.

Adam Grimley (11)
Bexley Grammar School

In The Woods

In the woods leaves rustle,
Twigs crack, trees groan.

In the woods ghosts crawl
Trees shake, leaves fall.

In the woods a wooden cage,
Shrieks with coldness
Breaks with the wind.

In the woods you're never in light
You're always in the dark.

Didier Nuttall (11)
Bexley Grammar School

Love

Love is passionate and powerful
Love can be strong but harmful
Love is loyalty and lawful
Love is graceful.

Love is unbelievable and forever
Love is fantastic and trustworthy
Love is beautiful and joyful
Love causes hatred.

Love is destructive and tiring
Love is worthwhile and caring
Love is obsessive and giving
Love is about sharing.

Love is for your family
Love is for your friends
Love is for your pets
Love is for your boy.

And most of all, love is for you.

Rebecca Clack (13)
Bexley Grammar School

The Forest

Looking up at the dark night sky,
Soft green grass at my feet.

As I walk through a pitch-black screen
My eyes begin to weep.

My pupil's getting bigger,
That sound's getting clearer.

For it's the animals around me,
Getting nearer and nearer and nearer!

Josh Carter (11)
Bexley Grammar School

The Party Thieves

Out came the sun,
as the guests had fun.
The entertainment was great,
for they'd been longing for this date.

The food was cooking,
there were seven chocolate cakes.
When no one was looking,
they disappeared from the plates.

The children were giggling,
and guiltily wriggling.
With their faces full of crumbs,
the guests knew they were the ones.

'Oh my God,
what have you done?
First there were seven,
and now there are none!'

The children felt sick,
their stomachs were full.
They'll share the cakes next time,
and not eat them all.

Alex West (12)
Bexley Grammar School

A Night In Twilight Wood

The sparkle of the stars
Better than Mars,
You can see in Twilight Wood.

When the trees move
I'm sure she'll approve,
With a kiss in Twilight Wood.

Lysander loves Hermia,
Hermia loves Lysander.
They ran away
To Twilight Woods.

To get away from Demetrius,
Hermia's admirer
And to make the dreams
All come true . . .

But the Twilight Wood isn't normal,
It's magical
Chants and sparks
As fairies
Make it alive!

Natasha McLellan (11)
Bexley Grammar School

No More

Tired . . . of having to be like this
Tired . . . of feeling this way
Tired . . . of wanting you so badly
Tired . . . of needing your attention
Tired . . . of pretending
No more.

Tired . . . of having to act like this
Tired . . . of feeling so hurt
Tired . . . of wanting what I can't have
Tired . . . of needing your touch
Tired . . . of living in the past
No more.

Tired . . . of having to hide
Tired . . . of feeling the pain of a broken heart
Tired . . . of wanting a chance
Tired . . . of needing your touch
Tired . . . of tears on my pillow
No more.

Tired . . . of feeling empty
Tired . . . of wishing for nothing
Tired . . . of wanting to cry
Tired . . . of needing to lie
Tired . . . of dying inside
No more.

Once there was a young girl
Lost in her lover's eyes
She would die for him
Lie for him
Cry for him
She was . . forever his
No more.

No more.

Michelle Tran (14)
Bexley Grammar School

Trapped Emotion

I'm fighting this feeling inside,
No matter how hard I try,
No matter how hard it gets,
It won't go away.

What do I do to ignore it inside me?
Do I follow my instincts blindly?
Do I let it all out?
Do I let it all go?

To ignore it, will make it grow stronger,
And to go blindly seems senseless.
If I let it out, I might get hurt,
If I let it go, I might break.

When I talk to you,
It's hard to talk,
When I listen to you,
It's hard to listen.

This feeling is rising inside,
It's taking over me,
I can't get out of this state of mind,
I can't let it go.

Every time I speak to you,
I begin to choke,
Every time I see you,
I begin to go blind.

Maybe it's best if I ignore you,
Maybe it's best if I don't see you,
Maybe it's best if we don't talk,
Maybe it's best for the both of us.

Sarah Lovell (13)
Bexley Grammar School

The Ball

Everybody came from far away,
They'd been travelling all through the day.
Everyone arrived in horse-drawn carts,
Carrying gifts shaped like hearts.

The women wore glamorous frocks,
With their gorgeous long locks.
The men wore pin-striped suits,
And their long black boots.

White balloons were scattered around,
Whilst the couples danced round and round.
Pink confetti would be dropped at night,
It was such a wonderful sight.

The food was looking rather yummy,
So everyone stuffed their tummy.
The cake was three tiers high,
There was also an apple pie.

Lucy Beaumont (11)
Bexley Grammar School

I Wish . . .

I wish I were a gasping cheetah covered in crimson and
                                        chrome jewels.
I wish I were aqua diamonds on a violet slug.
I wish I were a whale, hard and sharp as a flint, with a tongue
                                        covered in sapphire gems.
I wish I were a solitary platypus with turquoise ornaments as a coat.
I wish I were a cat with white pearls for whiskers.
I wish I were a fish with burgundy trinkets for eyes.
I wish I were a diamond that looked like a golden horse.
I wish I were blue and looked like a pearl dog.
I wish I were a ruby that was an emerald chicken.
I wish I were a gem that looked like a magenta zebra.

Gurmangal Singh Dhillon (11)
Bexley Grammar School

The Party

It's finally here, the party of the year
All I want to do is give the biggest cheer
Good parties these days are so very few
I'm so excited my outfit's brand new

The guests are arriving and the DJ is ready
Friends and family are coming, including Freddie
My name in big letters with an eighteen beside
Lots of boxes with presents inside

The decorations are hanging
And the music is banging
The champagne is flowing
And the lights are all glowing

Everyone wanted a piece of the cake
Because it was made of chocolate flake
All good things come to an end
Goodbye family and my friends.

Selen Mindikoglu (11)
Bexley Grammar School

The Forest

Standing tall
The trees are like hands trying to grab me.
The moon, the stars,
Shine out bold to guide me,
For I may get lost -
If to fear the worst -
And the unknown animals may attack me!

Eyes, big like saucers, staring,
Watching me as I weave in and out of the trees.
The darkness surrounds me,
Closing me in,
Fighting its way through the crowd to get me!

Alexandra Button (11)
Bexley Grammar School

Let's Go

We are off to a party,
There will be lots of girls,
With annoying pink dresses,
And hair all done in curls.

We are off to a party,
Sausages, sandwiches and cake,
Lemonade, coke and secret beer,
Will we end up with a tummy ache.

We are off to a party,
Balloons and streamers everywhere,
Red, yellow and blue shining lights,
Decorations done with flair.

We are off to a party,
Rock music, garage and hip-hop,
Dancing, moving, singing,
Let's keep partying till we drop.

Andrew Vincent (11)
Bexley Grammar School

In The Dark, Dark Night

In the dark, dark night,
I see the moon and the stars
And the branches waving in the wind.

In the dark, dark night,
I see a pair of eyes staring at me
While I hear weird and scary noises.

In the dark, dark night,
I get a frightening feeling
Something is out there, stalking me
Waiting to pounce!

Charley Stuart (11)
Bexley Grammar School

The Party Poem

I've been around the world
Know the place inside out
Seen what to see
Been where to be

But there's a party
With a fabulous cake
I don't know how
The cook did bake

Smiling faces
All around
Flashing lights
From downtown

There were so many people
The party was big
There was a gigantic crowd
The music was loud

The guests brought lots of bling, bling
All the children did was sing, sing
The clock struck twelve - ding, ding
The telephone rang - bring, bring

It was the MOBOs
Nelly singing
Usher blinging
I'm a VIP, my name's R Kelly.

Asif Chowdhury (11)
Bexley Grammar School

The Swan

The smooth eyelids of the swan yawned and unfurled swiftly.
Calm
Fresh was the air that glided against the swan's fluffy, glorious
Feathers
The feeble water creatures dare not to step into the swan's territory
Fear
The swan . . .

Pure beauty
Swish, swash . . . splish, splosh goes the sound of the water
which is oxygen to the swan
Sheer pleasure comes from bopping around the water
Heaven
The once ugly duckling boasts its beauty to former bullies
Gloating
The swan
Unique.

Fatima Bashira (12)
Bexley Grammar School

Bear

I see it now,
Its long nose protruding out of the dense, thick, vibrant forest.
It heaves the rest of its body out of the trees,
Glistening and shimmering with the early morning dew,
Imperious and majestic,
Calm and collected,
Soft and warm.
Its deep eyes stare unblinkingly towards me,
Like deep puddles of water troubled and fearful.
It is in a clearing surrounded by a blanket of trees
Swallowing it up like clouds over a full moon.
Its black fur covers it and gently it sways and ripples
Like waves on a distant bay
As it turns to leave I know . . .
It's a bear.

Charlie Boyles (12)
Bexley Grammar School

Lady Ashbrook's Party

Only the distinguished and grandest
Were invited to attend the ball
At Lady Ashbrook's request
To be held at the hall

Outside there was rain
But inside was a glow
As clowns and jesters entertained
And put on a show

Inside were decorations and lights
Red, white and yellow
Everyone said they were a lovely sight
The music was soft and mellow

As darkness fell
And time came to say cheerio
There was much to tell
From those who got to go.

James Peeney (11)
Bexley Grammar School

Cactus

Cactus
green
burnt amber
brown
red
cactus
depressed
alone
individual
unasked
unhappy
over shadowed
cactus.

Fiona Hennessy (11)
Bexley Grammar School

Party Poem

Come to the party it's a beautiful sight
People wearing red, yellow and white
Fluffy feathers in their beautiful hair
But bring your own clothes, we have nothing to spare

The entertainment is fantastic
All the dancers seem really elastic
Little children are excellent at singing
Which one of them sees a dancer spinning

The place is covered in twirls and stars
It's as bright as head lamps on brand new cars
The glow of a candle on a guest's face
Makes something seem special about this place

Bowls of fruit and chocolate cake
Come to see what the cook really makes
Goose, duck, pig, turkey and lots, lots more
But remember not to swallow an apple core.

James Lee (12)
Bexley Grammar School

The Magical, Moving Forest

In the forest it is dark and still
But when I really listen it gives me a chill
I hear the beasts chanting songs
I see the birds with talons like tongs
And the trees I see
Are waving at me
But when I look down
I may have a frown
Because the forest floor
Looks ever so more
Like it's moving!

Max Hudson (11)
Bexley Grammar School

The Party

The party's full of people
All wearing suit and gown
Everyone is laughing
Not a single frown.

In the giant feast hall
The caterers all crowding round
Checking all the cutlery
The food is piled in mounds.

I really shouldn't be here
I'm going to be caught out
A guard's going to see me
And then he'll scream and shout.

Just one more look
She must be here somewhere
Why can't I find her?
I guess she's not in there.

Jake Palmer (11)
Bexley Grammar School

The Magical Wood

On this magical night,
Where stories unfold,
This enchanted wood
Has secrets to hold.

The twisted trees
Where the full moon glows,
The leaves fall down,
Where the river flows.

All alone
There I stood,
Seeing the wonder of
This magical wood.

Stephanie Lau (11)
Bexley Grammar School

The Hedgehog And The Hero

The pain was too unbearable to last
Oh, if only he had been a second later
If only he could turn back the hands of time
Then he could make things better

His leg dragged behind him
Leaving a trail of blood
His spikes were broken above him
Snapped at the stem, hanging lifelessly

From the car, the hedgehog looked dead
It was hardly moving
'Mum, Mum, stop the car,' he said
As the brakes squealed to a halt

He ran as fast as he could
A bit of movement, it wasn't dead!
She ran along behind him, blind to the crawling traffic
'Tim, what are you doing?' she said

He was bent over the animal
His hands were as red as wine
But he didn't care, it had to be alive
'Don't die' was all that was running through his mind

The hands were strong around him
As Tim lifted him off the floor
The pain was too excruciating
But he knew he was safer with Tim
He knew he was safer than before

Tim carried it to the car
He knew he didn't have much time
Thankfully, it wasn't far
The engine roared as they pulled away

As its breaths slipped slowly away
Tim held it close to his chest
'Don't worry, we'll be home soon'
'No!' Tim cried, but he knew he had done his best.

Georgina Bradley (12)
Bexley Grammar School

Seasons

Seasons, seasons, joy of the year,
Every year a new event,
Something new, something old.

Leaves turn from green to yellow,
Then back again.
The trees lose their leaves and then start to shiver,
Then when spring returns,
Their coats are glossy and bright.
Birds come from far away to celebrate springtime.
Then when the seasons change again,
They disappear.

Insects wake up and caterpillars are eating away,
The butterflies open their wings and fly off in a hurry,
They know they have to lay their eggs before spring is done.

The sun is like an oven, forever forking out heat,
The birds, insects and even people head for the beach.
The fish jump up for joy, at the heat of the sun,
Then depart under the waves to cool down in the darkness.
The sun continues giving out heat, making our skin darker.
All the flowers, summer ones, are out now,
Yellow, blue, orange, red, the list is endless.
All for the drunken bees who love their flowery scent.

The seasons start all over again, year after year,
Joys of spring, summer, autumn and winter are to be seen again.

Rebecca Whitter (13)
Bexley Grammar School

The Forest Of Forever

Enchanted with excitement
The beautiful wood,
No man or beast ever could
Find the magic within the trees.
Gently the wind blows a midsummer breeze,
Unknown, mysterious, dark unseen.

The forest of wonders, just like a dream
Maybe it is, I just can't tell.
I hear ringing, the sound of a bell
It could be the pixies,
It could be the fairies
Casting their spells, all through the night.
If you find them
I bet you'll never
But anything can happen in the Forest of Forever.

Jessica Lawrence (11)
Bexley Grammar School

The Ginger Ninja

He stalks his prey,
Waiting, watching,
The ginger ninja,
Waiting to pounce,
The moment to pounce is near,
Suddenly,
He pounces,
Onto his prey,
Ripping, tearing his way through the flesh,
The prey goes limp,
He eats his prey,
Chomp, chomp, chomp,
He sneaks through the jungle,
Back to his family,
His prey is a zebra,
He is a tiger.

Tom Yardley (12)
Bexley Grammar School

My Fish

I have a fish called Paul,
Who is oh so very small,
And rounder than a ball,
And rougher than a wall.
I found him in the sea,
He was swimming next to me,
He is always happy,
And likes to kiss fleas.
He doesn't look so scary,
And his body is very hairy,
He can get weary,
He is a non-scary, hairy, weary fish.
He eats anything that's blind,
He doesn't eat his own kind . . . fish,
He likes to take care of his body and mind,
And takes yoga lessons at any time.
He is as quiet as a cat,
And chased my rat . . . Pat.
He sometimes sleeps on my mat
And wears a small top hat.
He is my fish,
Yes, my fish.

Bosun Kamson (12)
Bexley Grammar School

Dark, Dark Wood

Branches hung above like claws,
Nothing could be heard but the shrill noise of silence
Filled with love and hate.
The moon shone down, casting its silver pearl light,
Creatures of the night glided through the air and scuttled
on the ground.
The stars shone, glimmering faintly between thick foliage,
The thick stifling hot air
Heated the emotions of all within.

Hugo Humphreys (11)
Bexley Grammar School

The Amazing Tiger

He stretches, he yawns
A new day begins
His hunger stirs and motivates
The predator emerges watchful.

Under the sunlight
The golden creature appears ever vigilant
Through the crackling grass
The golden eyes stare.

The sun dances on his stripes
Tawny eyes ablaze
The antelope becomes aware
There is no time to graze

Through the tall grass
He silently stalks
He has no time for playing
No time for strolls and walks

Suddenly the roaring breaks through
The cruel fate of the prey
So sleek and new
Is sealed this sunny day

A wondrous creature - the tiger
A hunter now
And for evermore.

Joshua Hoggan (12)
Bexley Grammar School

Tarantutrap

The humid temp,
The humid time.
Through it goes,
Through thick green slime.

The slime is the jungle,
The jungle is slime.
In its home it waits,
And waits for its time.

The time has come,
The trap has been sprung.
Now after what happened,
The commotion is gone.

The fangs go in,
The venom trickles out.
The prey is dead,
No scream, no shout.

Edward Anderson (12)
Bexley Grammar School

The Forest

Forests are scary
Animals are hairy,
They're disgusting and sick
And tremendously thick.
In the forests, trees grow so big
And so do the brown twigs.
The grass is so long, it needs a good trim
And in the river, you can have a good swim.
The leaves are as green as an apple
And when they fall off, they crackle.
The logs are all broken off
And the smell may make you cough.

Charlie Ludlow (12)
Bexley Grammar School

Bulldog Poem

Red, white and blue
If you're British, the bulldog is the dog for you
He eats a full English out of a dish
He pummels the ground as he practically flies
And he looks at his dinner, with beady eyes
His woof is loud
Very unlike a coward's
His colours are plain but easy to spot
But unadventurous and boring, he is not
He's strong, hungry, lazy and mean
I give him anything he needs
He normally has a siesta
After his usually Friday night fiesta
In a boxing ring
He is the king
He punches and clobbers
And also slobbers.

He is my cool dog,
My bulldog.

Christopher Plummer (12)
Bexley Grammar School

I Wish . . .

I wish I were a kangaroo in the snow playing pool.
I wish I were a dog surfing in the midday sun.
I wish I were an elephant skating in the breeze,
I wish I were a fish in the rain, playing hockey.
I wish I were a monkey playing chess in the sun.
I wish I were a snake playing rugby in the frost.
I wish I were a swan, playing water polo in the fog.
I wish I were a rabbit playing netball in the misty cloud.
I wish I were a frog playing football in a storm.
I wish I were a badger in the wind, playing tennis.

Charlotte Nelson (11)
Bexley Grammar School

Blow The Wind From The Willows

Once a man,
He wrote about,
A fearsome four,
Without a doubt.

Toad outside was pretty plain,
But inside he was rather vain,
His fortune made him very bold,
But by the others he got told.

Now Badger was a mighty beast,
And in his time ate many a feast,
Strong as an ox was Badger the bold,
But wise as an owl as he grew old.

Ratty was a river banker,
Happy with life; he dropped his anchor,
Love he did all boats and water,
But his love for his friends was none the shorter.

Moley now was a lovely creature,
Kind at heart, a kindness preacher,
He lived deep down below the ground,
Until he joined Ratty, a new friend found.

Now these four rogues,
Each hauled separate loads,
But joined up together,
On life's long road.

On life's long road,
They stood up for Mr Toad,
The defeated the weasel crew,
And the Wind from the Willows they blew.

Robert Ashcroft (13)
Bexley Grammar School

The Killer Whale

Deep below, in the dangerous sea,
A mysterious creature you may see.
It swims with much grace,
That is with some haste.
But when prowling for a feast,
It acts like a beast.
It eats up the ground,
Without making a sound.
It stalks its prey,
At the bottom of the bay.
A seal it eats,
It's full of meat.
If one day you're at sea,
In the right place you may be,
You will catch a glimpse of this thing,
But watch out, it may spring.
Its calling is strident,
Like being hit with a trident.
This creature I speak of,
A killer whale.

Alex Fernandes (12)
Bexley Grammar School

Hunny Bunny

I am a bunny called Hunny,
Which I don't find very funny,
I am black and fluffy,
And the top of my head is tufty,
I have a double chin,
Where my neck should have been,
Life is unfair,
When you have too much hair.

My home is a hutch,
This isn't much,
But I have a run,
Which I find fun.

All I'm fed is seeds,
But what I really need
Is a carrot or two,
As this keeps my coat new.

The fox comes to scare me,
But he can't get near me.
My life is great,
But all I need is a mate.

Keren Selby (13)
Bexley Grammar School

Thanks For Nothing

T hanks for nothing Dad,
H ave you forgotten us?
A ll the things you left behind,
N othing for your son to turn to,
K nowing you forgot me, hurt me,
S ons can't be left behind.

F orgotten,
O ver,
R uined.

N othing left of you,
O nly memories of the past,
T here are no reasons for why you left,
H ow you felt, but
I don't care, I don't want you,
N othing,
G o!

Ysobel Solly (11)
Bexley Grammar School

The Cheetah

The cheetah sprints, the cheetah sprints,
The cheetah sprints through the jungle.

The cheetah sees, the cheetah sees,,
The cheetah sees his prey in the jungle.

The cheetah chases, the cheetah chases,
The cheetah chases, he chases in the jungle.

The cheetah pounces, the cheetah pounces,
The cheetah pounces on his prey in the jungle.

The cheetah kills, the cheetah kills,
The cheetah kills his prey in the jungle.

The cheetah eats, the cheetah eats,
The cheetah eats his prey in the jungle.

Anne Akintola (12)
Bexley Grammar School

The Beauty Of The Wood

There was a peaceful breeze,
That whistled between the trees,
And the buzz of the bees
Drifted through the eve.
The moon shimmered,
And the dew glimmered.
As the little people crept,
To everywhere charm leapt.
The beauty of the night,
Dispelled all fright.
Everything was pure as moonlight.
And the lakes' waves
Swept through glistening caves.
In it you could see the moon's gleam,
In a midsummer night's dream.

Joshua Lansdell (11)
Bexley Grammar School

The Hedgehog

The hedgehog scampered across the road
Using its knowledge of the Green Cross Code
But when a car came along
All it could hear was death's song
His life flashed before it
Back to when it lived in a pit
It thought of its family
Back to when it ate apples called Bramley
It remembered the fun it had
Even when it was bad
Back to when it weaved between every tree
And when it used to scrape its knee
So he made a decision
That his life was a mission
To play games and have fun
And as he went to Heaven he saw a nun.

Connor Carey Jones (13)
Bexley Grammar School

Dolphins

Gracefully, he swims behind the boat,
following the waves
up and down, up and down.
Behind him, others join him,
diving sleekly.

A greyish-blue tint
in the open sea
of dolphins, bobbing
beneath the calm waters,
gently gliding
across the vast ocean.

A high-pitched squeak
as they swim away.
Krill and plankton hide
amongst the sea anemones
while the dolphins swoop down
hungrily.

Sophie Morton (13)
Bexley Grammar School

Memories

Memories can be good and bad
Some are just flashbacks but some are sad
Going to my nan's swimming pool
Swimming around with all my cousins
Or my last day at primary school
A sad day but somehow still fun
We got in limo outside the gate
We sat inside thinking about things we'd done
Going to the Isle of Wight
We'd play games all day
Then stay up all night
Those are memories of my past
It's such a shame they didn't last!

George James (11)
Bexley Grammar School

Dragon

This creature lurks in the shadows
waiting until its prey comes
and then suddenly a burst of fire
comes out of the night
and roasted the dragon's prey.

The creature silently moves
about the pitch-black caves
searching for its next victim
and it could strike at any moment.

The creature eats until it dies
its life is not worth living
it is diving through many underground systems
it can swim through water like stems.

Because it is a loner
it will like lots of doners.

The dragon.

Samuel Shepherd (12)
Bexley Grammar School

Destroyer

The sea surrounds them as they lie
Exhausted on this tin can, they call a ship.
The Destroyer, it's called, a name's no lie
Destroyer of their haphazard kinship.

The sea surrounds them as they try,
Shells bombarding the ship.
Destroyer, destroyer of lives,
Hits the enemy, stings like a whip.

The sea surrounds them as they die,
No time for one last quip.
No longer can they defy
Destroyed - destroyed by the ship.

Alexander Soutar (13)
Bexley Grammar School

Flea

He says his last farewells
And bounces across the fur
As he jabs and drinks
Blood all the way

He takes along run-up
And he leaps
Taking off like a plane
Picking up speed all the time

The runway of his new home is in sight
And he jerks
Slamming on the brakes
For an erratic landing

He gazes at his new home
And he takes a big, juicy bite
And he takes a big and chewy bite
And causes a yelp of pain as loud as a foghorn
Can you guess who he is?
He's a flea.

Steven Ruffhead (12)
Bexley Grammar School

I Wish . . .

I wish that I could play cricket in the rain on a mountain,
I wish that I could play in a storm on a school roof.
I wish that I could play tennis in the sun, at Wimbledon.
I wish that I could play rugby in the snow, on a muddy field.
I wish that I could play basketball in the wind on the grass,
I wish that I could play snooker in the jungle, in the rain.
I wish that I could swim in the freezing cold sea,
I wish that I could play volleyball on the beach, in the snow.

Jack Plows (11)
Bexley Grammar School

Fox

He is running, he is running
Through the town, through the town
Passing homes of many, passing homes of many
Running, running, running
All the same, all the same
Bushy tails, bushy tails
Burrows as homes, burrows as homes
Tips and dumps, tip and dumps
Is what they survive on, is what they survive on
Eating, eating, eating
Waste, waste, waste
W`hat are they doing? What are they doing?
Wrong, wrong, wrong
You keep hunting, you keep running
Stop,
Stop,
Stop,
He is only *fox.*

Rachel Young (13)
Bexley Grammar School

The Dark, Dark Wood

D own in the dark wood the trees are rustling
A t night shadows look like claws
R ound colossal eyes of animals, frightening
K eep still and quiet or the animals will have you

D anger lurks all around
A ggressive noises sounding around me
R ustle, rustle, how scared am I?
K neeling down I try to hide

W ould I be lost forever
O bserving my surroundings
O bviously I wouldn't survive . . .
D own in the dark, dark wood.

James Ross (11)
Bexley Grammar School

Snake

The snake sneaked silently
through the field.
A ruthless creature,
it had to kill.

He saw a rabbit,
he chased and chased.
He found it hiding
in a dark, dark place.

He showed no mercy,
he had to eat.
He struck with venom,
at this tasty treat.

The snake sneaked silently
through the field.
A ruthless creature
it had to kill.

Oliver Taylor (12)
Bexley Grammar School

Frozen

The smell of sea air
We're here!
I run onto the beach
The sun beating down on me,
I bound into the sea.
So wet, so glistening, so . . .
'Argh! Cold, so cold!'
I sprint back to shore
My toes are numb,
I dive into a towel
And sit, shivering, grumpy and thawing.
Mum appears with an ice cream and I sit up,
'You're too grumpy to eat ice cream!' says Mum.
'Me, grumpy?' I lick happily. 'Never!'

Alex Levey (11)
Bexley Grammar School

A Midsummer Nightmare!

'Twas midsummer when we went,
Out of Athens to be free.
Escaping our harsh punishment,
But it was too dark to see.

The trees were whispering secrets,
Discreetly judging us.
The moon was out of sight, that night,
It was definitely past dusk.

The bushes quietly rustling,
Eyes were everywhere.
Insects in our shoes,
In our shirts, our nose, our hair.

So what was a simple task,
To put on a royal play,
Ended in terror,
As we screamed from night till day.

Liam Shipton (11)
Bexley Grammar School

Schooldays

32 people
12 books
You do the maths.

Sometimes it's good,
Sometimes it's bad,
Sometimes it's happy or sad.

But when you get the right
Chemistry,
When you get the flow -
You know.

That when you start
Your new school,
You'll be okay!

Hayley Pain (11)
Bexley Grammar School

Willie's Time

I came to the door and met the giant,
As tall as a giraffe,
And as fat as a king.

He was incalculable, immeasurable,
He scared me to death.

I tried to make friends with him,
He became my friend.

His name was Tom,
He wasn't like my mum.

He took me to town,
He gave me a pound.

Tom was so kind too,
As kind as someone could be.

I went to the farm, I went to the shops,
This was the best day during May.

I thought it was all a dream,
He wasn't so mean.

I felt like giggling,
And was jumping with glee.

David Akinwunmi (11)
Bexley Grammar School

The Beach

Sunny, bright and boiling hot,
The sun blazing the sand and sea,
People sweating and dehydrated.

Waves crashing up the shore,
Splishing, sploshing on the sand,
Roaring sound as it rushes up.

Rocks rushed swiftly up the shore,
Rounded pebbles rolling up and down,
Pieces of broken seashells everywhere.

The sand sizzling hot,
Burning your feet as you walk,
The wind blowing it along the shore.

The breeze blowing in your face,
You smell the salty water,
And hear seagulls chipping and chirping.

People relaxing on the beach,
Laughing and joking as they speak,
Everyone has a good time,
Especially at the beach.

James Hoang (13)
Bexley Grammar School

The Lake District

Every spring when the snow has melted
Me and my dad, we go to the Lake District
With its mountains so high
And lakes so deep.

We climb the crags and mountains
Carrying rucksacks on our backs
Whatever weather, rain or sun
We are always up for the challenge.

We stay in youth hostels
From the best to the worst
Even the most remotest
With everything in our backpacks.

We have got proper equipment
So we will survive
Even in the wind, rain or snow
We will reach the summit, no matter what.

We often get lost
Or get pushed back, but
With my dad's GPs and my great directional senses
We will always be back in time for tea.

Bart Challis (13)
Bexley Grammar School

The Lion

Spreading out his knife-like claws
Beneath the long grass crouching low
Widening his terrifying jaws
Prowling round nice and slow.

Swishing his long tail
Glaring at his prey
With his pride watching he could not fail
Unaware of this hunter, the zebra lay.

Onwards and onwards he crept
Towards his target aim
And out of his cover he leapt
Through the air like a burning flame.

Through the flesh his claws and teeth sunk in
The zebra squealing with terror and pain
The sound of the tearing of the zebra's skin
Blood absorbing into the lion's mane

And so his pride watched with pleasure
As the corpse was dropped to the ground
They violently attacked their treasure
And as the king watched, he stood tall and proud.

Bonnie-Marie Abhayaratne (13)
Bexley Grammar School

My Teacher

My teacher is wicked
My teacher is cool
My teacher is a star
My teacher is tall
My teacher is wacky
My teacher is a clown
My teacher's always happy
My teacher wouldn't frown
My teacher does ballet
My teacher does rock
When she said she plays bowls
It gave us one big shock
My teacher is exciting
My teacher is fun
My teacher is the best
She's way out, number one
My teacher is a painter
She's really good at art
She's good at nearly everything
Except for dressing smart
My teacher hates eggs
My teacher hates toast
My teacher hates broccoli
My teacher hates roasts
I'm going to miss our teacher
Because she's so cool
Next year I'm going to think of her
When I go to secondary school.

Josie Charles (11)
Bexley Grammar School

The Dark Wood

Silence filled the darkened air,
No room to move, speak or stare.
Little light passed through the trees,
The ground sheltered by its blackened leaves.

The sudden sound from beneath the foot
Made you stop, turn and look.
But naught could be seen,
Except the darkness, thick and mean.

Then a brightened clearing comes into sight,
You're blinded by the moon's strengthened might.
Little flickers of light go by,
Making you look, gasp and sigh.

Then the specks of light fly away,
But all you do is stand and stay.
Slowly the light begins to fade
You just think of the story that has been made.

Lee Dunmore (11)
Bexley Grammar School

Where Should I Go?

In the depth of night the moon is shining bright,
In a prison of trees,
In fear, I freeze.

The trees of the deep dark woods,
Stand tall with leafy hoods.
I did not know
Where to go!

Jack Bates (11)
Bexley Grammar School

Untitled

I glide silently through the water,
Camouflaged to everyone, everything,
Graceful, like a bird of prey.
I am feared, deadly, agile, fast,
Dangerous, like a stealth bomber,
Undetectable.

My fin penetrates the air,
Above the surface,
My victim panics,
Flapping its limbs in vain.

I circle my prey, waiting,
Waiting for the right time,
I strike.
My victim drifts slowly down,
Dinner!

Chris Hughes (13)
Bexley Grammar School

The Dark Woods

A visit to the woods was the place to go,
It came to my mind when I was feeling low,
So I went there in the cold and miserable night,
Who knew it could be such a fright,
On my own in the cold, foggy mist,
Feeling some tingles on my wrist,
I walked a few steps forward and then heard a noise,
Must have been me or a group of boys,
I stopped to look around me,
But no people could I see,
I got a bit scared so I walked back home,
Next time I think I shouldn't go alone,
I was getting relieved that I was nearly there,
If another thing happened to me it would be a nightmare,
I reached home not wanting to go away,
It was time to go to bed and lay.

Srikesh Datta (11)
Bexley Grammar School

My Journey In The Forest

I'm near the gate
but I'm still thinking.
Is the forest safe,
would I get lost?

So I go through the forest
and the cold, peaceful breeze
travels through the scary trees.
The dust travels from the ground
up in the air, circling round.

The smell of the midsummer rain
the crunch of the twigs,
I can hear a sound
from the rustling leaves.
The circled, round moon
sets a white blanket on the trees.

A bunch of golden stars
high up in the sky,
shines their bright light
like they're giving me a message.

I can taste the fresh air
rolling on my tongue
freezing my fingers
until they go numb.

I can see the dark green leaves, dancing or waving.
The over-full bin falls on the ground with a big bang.

I'm just about to step out of the forest
so I closed the gate.
Now I'm freezing cold
I can't wait until I get in
my cosy warm bed.

Daniel Akanni (11)
Bexley Grammar School

The Seasons Of A Year

Winter

C reeping, cold, eerie, dark, dreary
O paque, silent night sky
L ips blue with frostbite
D ead, dull, dooming voices.

Spring

Where there was once rain
Now sunshine
Flowers blooming.

Autumn

Where there was once sunshine
Now rain
Dead leaves gathered on the ground
Naked trees
Shining wet faces wading through a sea of dry auburn leaves
Red and browns.

Summer

H umid, breathless temperatures
O h the sun is beating down effortlessly
T he air is busy, faces are sweaty.

Winter, spring, autumn, summer
The four seasons of a year.

Chantelle Datiari (11)
Bexley Grammar School

Five Young Men, Five Young Boys

Five young children
Five young boys,
Two of whom, as bright as the moon
Play with their own wooden toys.

One of the gang, called Sam,
Looked with a hungry face.
Then the other two boys
Who played with their toys
Gave him their toys in grace.

His frown vanished
And his envy vanquished
From his eye came a single tear,
As the other two boys, called Dick and Dan,
Decided to come near.
'Could I ride your bike?' said Dan.
Then Sam turned
His heart, they yearned
As he smiled, 'Of course you can!'

As the boys all giggled,
Their faces muddled.
The best of friends,
Chris, Jack, Sam, Dick and Dan.

Affan Besim (14)
Bexley Grammar School

X-Isle

He watches
If he stands still, they won't notice him
They never do
If he waits silently they won't hear him
They never do
If he grabs them they won't feel him
They never do
If he cuts their throats, they will feel no pain
They never do
If he ends the world a thousand times over, they will not know
They never do
If he hangs scythes in their bedrooms, they never notice
They never do
If he dies they won't care
They never do for he is an . . .
X-isle!

Connor Minnican (12)
Bexley Grammar School

I Wish . . .

I wish I were in the soft snow playing football in Italy,
I wish I were in a sandstorm playing basketball in the Sahara Desert.
I wish I were in the wind, playing tennis on the largest field in the world.
I wish I were in a downpour of rain, playing cricket in India,
I wish I were in a hurricane, playing golf in Spain,
I wish I were in the middle of a tidal wave, surfing in Scotland.
I wish I were in hailstones swimming in the Pacific Ocean.
I wish I were in a heatwave skiing in Australia.
I wish I were in the blazing sun, ice skating on the River Thames.

Joey Hosier (11)
Bexley Grammar School

Beautiful Creatures

Some animals are enrapturing, here are the few
That I think are spectacular and I hope you do think so too.

The killer whale has streaks of blue across its back
With lightning yellow gleaming on top of its front.
On its fin, ruby really shows its glory.
In the sun there are no words to express
The beauty of this magnificent creature.

The monkey is a swift animal who sets it identity in the Amazon jungle.
The monkey is a perfect shade of bright emerald,
It shimmers and glimmers in the alluring sun.
The tail of this charming creature is crimson with shadows of black.
This slick creature is an outstanding creature.

The parrot totally adores scorching weather for it soars around Africa.
Indigo adorns the front of the parrot while orange
Criss-crosses the back.
Lavender and aqua fill the wings.
When the parrot flies it is a breathtaking sight.

Seun Olawale (11)
Bexley Grammar School

The Glistening Woodland

The clasping hands are shivering in the moonlight.
Eerie yellow eyes peeking from within the bushes.
A sudden thud awakes my attention.
The bars of this moonlight cage are closing in around me.
I feel as though I will be trapped forever, unless I find my way.
As I sit in this enchanting place, I can see pixies flying in and out.
While flying they leave rainbow sparks gleaming behind them.

Alexandra Smith (11)
Bexley Grammar School

Why?

Why does the cat have a tail?
Why is a shark not a whale?
Why does the bird have the gift of song?
Where are we going, where do we belong?
Why is the sea stuck to the shore?
Why can't we find an end to all war?
Why is the world so full of hate?
Why can't we fix this dreadful state?
Why is there not enough love, why's this the case?
Why don't people matter, why's it their race?
How long are we here, when are we leaving?
Why is there death, why is there grieving?
Why is this world so full of woe?
Who can we turn to, where can we go?
Why can't we make this a better place?
Full of love and eternal grace.

Julia Smith (11)
Bexley Grammar School

Animals That Need Love

Cats that purr when they want their food,
That hiss when they want to be left alone.
Dogs that bark when they're scared and lonely,
Want their food or want to come in
Through the locked, back door
And who pant when they like you.
Rabbits that prick up their ears
When a fox is coming to feed on its prey.
The rabbit jumps as fast as it can but then *thud!*
The fox walks, proud with its success, whilst
The rabbit lies there, dead!

Please give animals love and prevent this from happening.

Heather Fitzpatrick (11)
Cator Park School for Girls

Goose Eggs And Other Limericks

There was a young girl called Miss Bellow,
Who'd give anything for a marshmallow.
She thought that these sweets
Were the most scrumptious treats
Especially those soft and yellow.

There was an old man called Sir Tutter,
Who once had a craving for butter,
It was butter on toast
And butter on roast
He always was known as a nutter!

There was an old woman, Anne Drew,
She put apples and carrots in stew.
It tasted disgusting
And the cauldron was rusting
So she threw the lot down the loo!

There once was a boy called Ben,
Who never ate eggs from a hen.
He always ate goose eggs
With fruit juice and lamb's legs
And so did his brother named Ken.

Emma Pratt (11)
Cator Park School for Girls

Family

Family is about love and you caring for each other,
Family is about joy and happiness.
Family is about looking out for each other,
Family is about sharing and caring.
Family is about helping each other,
Family is about loving each other.
Family is about making your family laugh.
Family is about giving.
Families make us cry.

Rachel Carr (12)
Cator Park School for Girls

Autumn

I woke up this morning, what a day!
I looked out the window and it took my breath away.
A pretty landscape was what I saw
And how I wanted to explore much more,
So I put on my trousers,
Tied up my shoes.
I was so excited, there's so much to do!

I gathered conkers
And danced with the falling golden leaves.
So peaceful
My hair blowing in the breeze.

I was out there all day long,
But soon I lost track of time and
When I looked at my clock, it was one minute to nine!

My mother came out and gave me a hug,
She was so warm, so gentle and snug as a bug,
'It's time to come in now,' she said,
'It's getting late and it's time for bed!'

So as I lay dreaming of today,
The happiness that I feel now
Will never go away!

Sian Randolph (11)
Cator Park School for Girls

Kittens And Cats, Cats And Kittens

Kittens and cats
Lying on mats
Chewing on hats
Sitting on laps
Oh, I love kittens and cats

Chasing garden gnats
Killing mice and rats
Getting lots of pats
Licking up crumbs of your Kit-Kats,
Oh, I love kittens and cats

Prancing around flats
Scratching sacks
Some small, others fat
Run away from *bats!*
Oh, I love cats and kittens

Playing with oven mittens
Ouch! I've been bitten
What a job, cleaning their litter
Oh, I love cats and kitttens

They go to sleep once they've eaten
A kitten or cat should never be beaten
Cats and kittens are cute, it should be written
Cute, cute, cute cats and kittens!

I love cats and kittens.

Tayla Kelly (11)
Cator Park School for Girls

Gymnastics

Jumping high, jumping low,
Up and down on the trampoline,
Seat drops, front drops, turn around,
Jump up high, reach for the sky,
The trampoline is bouncy, I like it a lot.

Swinging, twisting all the time,
On the rings.
Turning upside down, turning round and round,
Jumping from two rings a lot of the time,
The rings are cool, I like them a bit.

Turning this way and that
On the balancing beam,
Cartwheels, round offs, front rolls too.
Jumps, twists, backflips and all.
The balancing beam is best,
I like it a lot.

Anna-Louise Johnson (12)
Cator Park School for Girls

Recipe For A Disaster

Spoon ten buckets of mud into a bowl,
Scatter two young animals, a puppy, perhaps a foal!
Grease a clean house, ready for chaos,
Then put ten children on a plate, ready for a toss.
Pour ten spoons of toxic fluids into a pot,
Then put on the heat till it's bubbling hot.
Leave this for two hours (disaster should be stirring).
Mix in a sprinkle of loud music, so you can have a sing.
Whip four crazy neighbours till they're *really* angry.
Then add a mad person called Shelly, Delphine or Lei,
Whisk them together and get faster and faster ,
And there you have it - a recipe for disaster!

Susanna Jenkins
Cator Park School for Girls

Poverty

You wake up in the morning, not a care in the world.
When there are people out there who are slaves
And being compelled to live a life of pain and sorrow,
Wondering if there will be a better tomorrow.

The pain and poverty those people have to live with,
Don't you ever think of all the things that you could give?
When you sit down about to have your tea
Do you ever feel sorry and think about the ones who are hungry?
Do you ever think whilst you're with your family
And all tucked up in your home, that there are people out there
Cold and alone?
When you take everything for granted or start to moan,
Think of all the people who really have a reason to be upset and groan.
Africa, India, Congo, Ethiopia and a lot more too,
Whilst you're wishing you had more money and clothes,
Think for a moment, who would be wishing to be you?

I hope you'll now be thinking, when you're cosy in your bed,
Of all the people who are sleeping in dirt and straw instead.

Shenelle Bardall (12)
Cator Park School for Girls

Beasts Of The Night

Night is the time when mysterious spirits play
Creatures, beings, roaming free
Night-time happenings lurking in the shadows
Sounds, noises, streak through the dark.

Daylight comes, what has happened, let us see?
Crime and vandalism has prowled our streets
Horrors of the night, nowhere to be seen.

Robyn Burge (12)
Cator Park School for Girls

Feelings

Have you ever felt really excited?
And you just want to scream it out
And it makes you shout.

Have you ever felt really sleepy?
And you just want to go back to bed,
Then you look in the mirror
And your face is all red.

Have you ever felt weak?
And you can't even go up the stairs,
And your mum gives you glares.

Have you ever felt really happy?
And it makes you want to jump up and down,
And it makes you want to go shopping in town.

Have you ever felt really nervous,
And it makes you feel shy,
And it makes you want to cry?

Chelsea Chandler
Cator Park School for Girls

What Is Red?

Red is danger
Red stands for anger
Red is our heart beating in our bodies
Red is the colour of an apple
Red is a sweet strawberry
Red is the colour that is filled with lots of love and happiness
Red stands for romance on Valentine's Day
Red is a colour that stands for family, fun and joy
Red is the colour of roses in springtime,
When all the flowers are growing.
Red is a gorgeous ruby ring
Red is a heart ribbon.

Janielle Duncan (13)
Cator Park School for Girls

Monday To Sunday, Are They Fun Days?

Monday is the day I start my week,
Do I then become a geek?

Tuesday, in lessons I concentrate,
For then, I can appreciate.

Wednesday, I do my homework till late,
I cannot go out with all my mates.

Thursday, I do karate,
But I also love going to parties.

Fridays, I get a star,
Maybe this will help me get far.

Saturday is when I rest,
That is when I feel the best.

Sunday, I pack my bags for school
To make sure I remember all my tools.

Chelsea Poynter (13)
Cator Park School for Girls

Love

Love is like a bird,
Love is like a flower,
Love is like two people connecting together.
When you talk about love,
What do you think it means?
When you think about love,
What do you think it means?
When you write about love,
What do you think it means?
Well to me,
Love is like a bird soaring high in the sky,
Love is like a flower growing in the soil.
Love is like two people connecting together.

Alexcia Gerald (14)
Cator Park School for Girls

The Perfect Shopping Trip

Start by weighing your limousine
Add to the pot,
Scatter your 500 kilos of mates
Across the pot evenly.
Put on the cooker and melt;
Every now and then, stir thoroughly,
Whilst you are melting, grate all your money,
And mix into the pot;
Now remove your melted mixture
And leave to cool;
Take your shopping mall,
And add spoons full of clothes,
Now pour carefully into the pot;
Put in the oven and leave to cook.
Don't forget to decorate,
With shopping bags and delicious pizza.
*Perfe*ct!

Delphine Lievens (11)
Cator Park School for Girls

Friday Night

I'm going out on a Friday night,
the mood is good, I feel alright.
Do my hair, paint my nails,
I'm having a party with all my girls.
Got a new dress,
have to dress to impress,
everyone's dancing, having fun.
It's gone past midnight, the party has begun,
my phone starts ringing, it's Mum on the phone.
She's wondering what time I'm gonna be home.
I get back late, in the morning
Mum goes mad and gives me a warning.
I'm grounded now for a week or two,
I can sneak out of the house, she won't have a clue.

Temeka James (13)
Cator Park School for Girls

Friends

Friends are people who make you laugh.
Friends are people who help you down the right path.
Me and my friends have a lot in common
Our friendship is like a bundle of sticks that can't be broken.

Yes, sometimes with friends we have our ups and downs,
But after a little talk we see smiles instead of frowns
It's a good sight to see and feel
It's almost like having a hearty good meal.

When you're bored and you pick up the phone
A friend will listen to all your jokes and moans
Just treasure it.

Good friends can be hard work
Sometimes you have to listen and agree just to keep it alive
But as time goes by and you have time to reflect
It's great to know you've given it your best!

Latoya Anderson (13)
Cator Park School for Girls

How To Make The Powderpuff Girls

To make the Powderpuff Girls, you will need a
Professor to do it for you but you have to instruct them.

Use three pots and label each of them either Bubbles,
Blossom or Buttercup.
Pour 100kg of sugar and spice in each pot.
Stir it in the pot, at the same time, tip in 333,000kg of everything nice.
Breakdown any lumps in everything nice.
Add a pair of giant's eyeballs in each pot,
Then stir without squashing the eyes.
In the pot labelled Buttercup, add 3 lbs of chemical X,
In Blossom's pot add 1.5 lbs and add 0.5 lbs to Bubble's.
Wait for five seconds, when those five seconds are finished,
They should fly out of their pots.
Now you have given birth to The Powderpuff Girls!

Jamilah Jahi (11)
Cator Park School for Girls

Peace In The World

Peace in the world,
Wouldn't it be nice to have peace in the world?
Peace, peace,
When will it come?
All this fighting, all this war,
Peace, when will it come?

People are crying,
People are dying.
Sad and all alone,
But someone is praying,
To send peace in the world.

The dove is arriving,
Spreading out peace into the world,
No one is crying,
Everyone is happy and content.

Mithunaa Nuges (11)
Cator Park School for Girls

Shopping Spree

Shopping, shopping, shopping spree
all these things for me, me, me.

Clothes and shoes,
there's nothing to lose,
what bag shall I choose?

I found a cute top, it was really cool,
when I tried it on, I looked a fool!

I found some jeans, they looked really good,
then I found a nice jumper with a hood.

There was lots of make-up I wanted to buy,
the lady said, 'Why don't you try?'

Time to pay at the till -
Oh my God, look at the bill!

Rosie Anne Jeffery (13)
Cator Park School for Girls

Shadow Eyes

One eye, then two
you can see glittering
all the way through.
First there, then not
darting past
then slowing a lot.

Coming and fading
through the trees,
there in the light,
by darkness it flees.
It follows you around
then is gone before anyone sees.

They run and they hide
but can't jump and shout.
They're taller in some lights
but gone when they're out.
They come and they go
that's what they're about.

Rebecca Ashton (12)
Cator Park School for Girls

Magic!

Something I have always liked . . . magic
I dream about it every night
Charming princes' girls in towers
Sprites and pixies dance for hours,
Flying carpet, chants and shells
Every story always tells . . . magic!

Disappearing funny trick . . . magic
Magicians or fairies; which will you pick?
Sparks and sprinkles
Stars that twinkle . . .
Talk about it, think it's lots
Is it real or is it not . . . magic?

Emily Sarrah Lahouel (12)
Cator Park School for Girls

I'm So Lucky

I'm so lucky I haven't had the experience,
The shouting and arguing
And the slamming of doors,
The abuse and swearing
And the pain in my mind.

I'm so lucky I haven't had the experience,
The crying and flames,
And grey choking smoke,
The black falling ashes,
And the pain in my body.

I'm so lucky I haven't had the experience,
No food and water,
None of the choices I have,
No freedom or fun,
And the pain in my heart.

I'm so lucky.

Olivia Holland (12)
Cator Park School for Girls

My Sister, My Friend and I

It was dark and it was cold,
The wind whistled and a story was told.
I heard a scream, I heard a yelp,
Someone was in need of help.
I ran, I stumbled,
I leapt, I tumbled.
I came to a lake, I came to a stream,
I saw one body and heard another scream.
Two were dead, a murderer alive,
I ran for it, my chance to survive.
I heard a shot . . .
Then I dropped.

My sister, my friend and I, in the silent dark,
All dead and alone in the windswept park.

Harriet Rogers (12)
Cator Park School for Girls

All Sports

Football
basketball
tennis is the best
we love all sports and we're
going to tell you about them.

Football
David Beckham is the best,
playing for Madrid is England's
worst regret.

Basketball
Is really fun when you can tackle them,
one by one.

Tennis
The tennis ball flies so high
when you hit it up to the sky.

Rugby Union
Has the ball pushing everyone
to the wall.

Cricket
Is a game that you don't play every day,
but when you do, the time will rush away.

Rounders
Running around when you hit the ball
against the ground.

All these games are really fun
but you *have* to play them, one by one!

Viktorija Lopato (12)
Cator Park School for Girls

Housewife

She irons the budgie, falls over the mat
Strangles the dog and kicks the cat
Pours tear in her coffee and sugar in her milk
Puts her smalls on cotton instead of Silk
Her cutlery in the drier and her washing in the drawer
Her rug is hanging on the wall
Her pictures are on the floor
Puts her rubbish in the oven
And her dinner in the bin
Puts her biscuits in a vase
And her flowers in a tin
Her quilt is in the bathroom
And her towels are on the bed
Her tools are in the living room
And her Hoover's in the shed
She sweeps the lawn and mows the yard
Her bacon's soft and her eggs are hard
Cleans the floor with a toothbrush
And her teeth with a mop
Comes home with the trolley
And leaves the kids in the shop
This mixed-up life of a housewife
Who helps you all she can
Haven't you lot guessed it yet?
This housewife is a man!

Louise Savage (15)
Cator Park School for Girls

Credit!

Every year I can't wait
For my summer to start
I shop, shop, shop for clothes
With my credit card

Skirts, tops, underwear and hats
That's what I buy
Shoes, make-up, jewellery
That's what I'd rather buy

Pink, yellow and lime
Summer colours at this time
Throw away the reds and blacks
The dull colours that don't match.

Yet I want more
But I know I can't
My mum will be mad
And cut my grant

Can't wait till next year
Just to shop again
To get more clothes
With the bank's interest.

Maria Savva (13)
Cator Park School for Girls

Sadness And Pain

As I sit there looking into his eyes,
all I can see is sadness and pain.
Tears running down his face like rain,
enough to make a river of pain.
As I sit there looking into his eyes,
Oh how I wish I could take all the pain away from him.
Let him be free of all the sadness and pain in his life.
Oh how I wish . . .
Let him be free!

Cassandra Gibbs (15)
Cator Park School for Girls

Life

They walk on fours and dribble
And then they walk on two
And then they walk on one leg more
And say, 'Why, where, what, who?'

On fours they laugh and splutter
Or make a great big noise,
And play and sing and listen to
Their favourite little toy.

On two they run and laugh and talk
And chat on their new phones,
And when they do not get their way
They moan and moan and moan!

And later in their own lives
When they still walk on two,
They go round all maturely
And go round looking blue.

And then eventually it comes
And then they walk on three,
And they now need some help in life
To walk on their wobbly knees.

The answer is in front of you
It's clearly Man on Earth,
From the oldest man to the youngest girl
Or the women giving birth.

Larissa Barnett (12)
Cator Park School for Girls

What Is A Crush?

When I have a crush, and think someone is cute,
I try so hard to contribute!
I could look and stare at him all day,
I only wish things could go my way!

We make eye contact, gazing into each other's eyes,
It's a moment I will never forget, I think I want to cry!
He's so sweet, kind, gentle and fit,
He probably thinks I'm such a twit!

He's good at everything, unlike me,
I can't even make a decent cup of tea!
I pluck up the courage to ask him out,
I hope he doesn't scream and shout!

My face is sour, as sour as a lime,
I say, 'Want to go out sometime?'
He looks at me, eyes open wide,
I wish I had a box to hide inside!

He opens his mouth, but no words at all,
I feel as fat as a football!
I'm in suspense and lots of rage.
I feel as though everyone's watching me
Like I'm on the stage!

He will say no, I have a girlfriend and
You're a mess, but he doesn't!
He says, *'Yes!*
Yes! Yes! Yes! Yes! Yes!'
He actually said, 'Yes!'

Charlotte Speer (13)
Cator Park School for Girls

Ocean Dream

The calm still waters rippling in the wind,
Like the creases in a soft, blue blanket,
Washing up against golden sand,
Gently foaming froth along its edges.

The turquoise calm keeping precious secrets,
Delving deep into blue unknown,
Sunlight dances on the surface,
Flecks of gold, shimmering with the waves.

The calming scent of the salty sea,
Rainbows of fish, flitter deep below,
Waves roar as they chase along the coast
A playful, purring kitten in disguise.

Like a fairytale, it gently unfolds,
A sparkling blue mystery,
A hidden magic, so great and intense,
This is my ocean dream.

Jessica Fitch Bunce (12)
Cator Park School for Girls

I'm In A Place

I'm in a place where the walls are built so high,
so high you can hardly see the sky.
I'm in a place where people hardly come out,
but always seem to come in.
I'm in a place where people never visit me,
to be honest it seems like they've forgotten about me.
I'm in a place where people have done different things
to get them where I am today, a place where orange
is the new 'in', and designers mean nothing
and the powerful pick on the weak for fun.
Guessed where I am yet?
Well as I lay on this hard prison bed, behind bars,
I close my eyes and dream of happier days instead!

Jessica Edun (13)
Cator Park School for Girls

The Mystery Key

In the bottom of the garden
Behind the rickety tree,
Underneath the plant pot,
I found a rusty old key.

'What's this key for?' I asked myself.
A door, some treasure, a gate?
It's probably nothing, I told myself,
Yet inside something told me, 'I'm sure that this is fate.'

Then suddenly behind my shoulder,
I heard a little shout,
And would you know it, it was a fairy.
All cute and little and stout.

She asked me for her key back,
I gave it to her straight away,
She said, 'Thank you very much!'
And fluttered far away.

That key must have been special
Cos fairies, you never do see,
But don't worry my dear fairy,
Your secret's safe with me!'

Lauren Ellis (12)
Cator Park School for Girls

My Soppy Dog

Slipper nicker,
Bone licker.
Tail wagger,
Toy dragger.
Meat eater,
Sloppy sleeper.
Fast runner
Great fun!

Charlotte Perkins
Cator Park School for Girls

My Mum

My mum is an average person you see,
she thinks, hurts, sees, needs, wants
and looks just like me

A mind as vigorous as can be and a heart as big as an oak tree x 3,
long wavy hair like the ocean sea and soft golden skin like the
Sahara sand under the delicate rays of the rising sun,
which makes me proud of my mum.

My mum is hilarious and glorious and
takes good care of all us.
She can be serious but at times that can be a good thing,
when she's in full swing and tells us to do every thing.

A good teacher, a preacher, who does her thing
and is willing to do anything for her loved ones.
Unity is her prosperity because I love her and she loves me
and we go together like 1, 2, 3 and ABC, as easy as can be.

When I'm around her and she's around me, we both see
the sun shine through.
Dealing and grieving for and with her problems too,
wow, how we made it!

She's back again, more stronger than ever
because of her brain.
My mum has overcome hills of bills and
has to keep the money going to be able to
put food on the table.

The stable lady who's life is so crazy right now!
My mum is such a loving soul and gives people energy,
and makes them smile whilst they're suffering the same as she has.
She lends a helping hand however still . . .

My mum is an average person you see, she thinks,
hurts, sees, needs, wants and looks just like me -
3, 2, 1 that's all - I'm done!

1, 2, 3, 4 there must be more to say, in each and every way
and every day I pray for the health and welfare of my mum.

Jahzmine Vassell (11)
Cator Park School for Girls

Goodbye

She said it,
Silence closed in after the words.
As I struggle with emotions,
She stares.
As I focus I begin to see
Her eyes are glazed and unmoving,
As if in a state of premonition,
Searching with her mind's eye.
For a flicker of a second,
Her eyes,
Cold and transparent,
But as the light moves,
They become a dancing ocean of colour.
They widen and dart
As she anticipates my reaction,
Studying,
Memorising,
Searching the planes of my face.
Her perplexed expression shows
My unreadable features,
Her eyes are pleading
For understanding,
Tears brimming,
Blurring her shimmering oceans.
I comprehend and nod slightly,
Her eyes crease in the corners,
She smiles
Through her tears.
Her hooded lashes hide her emotions from me,
As she walks away.
I step back, sigh and leave.

Monique Tulloch (13)
Cator Park School for Girls

The Land Of Make Believe

Golden sunshine, smooth, soft sand,
Children skipping hand in hand.
Swaying palm trees with large flat leaves,
All in my land of make believe.

Fairies dance and sing their song,
Children in bed, where they belong.
Cats curled up with dishes of cream,
It's all there in the world of dreams.

Rapunzel, princesses and the beautiful queen,
Animals hiding where they can't be seen.
Mossycoat, three pigs and the evil cook
Share their adventures in my fairy tale book.

Pens hit the page and hands start to write,
Angels and fairies in dazzling light.
Drawings and pictures in pride and glory
Are written together in a magical story.

Magical cats parade in the night,
Chinese Cinderellas with their feet bound tight.
My eyes start to open, we now have to leave
My beautiful land of make believe.

Caitlin Johnstone (14)
Cator Park School for Girls

The Phoenix

Rise from the ashes,
Up to the sky,
No one believes,
Unless seen with their eyes.

Tail licked by flames,
Beak bright as sunlight,
A mythological creature
That could reverse the night.

Healing tears,
Hypnotic eyes,
Royalty in their minds,
No reason for lies.

Bright red wing feathers,
Fiery yellow breast,
A loyal companion
Until their next death.

But are they real?
Have we been blinded by lies?
Possessed by what is here and now,
With a hollow heart we sigh.
The phoenix - not just a bird.

Michelle Ashton (13)
Cator Park School for Girls

Reflection

I'm someone who can't control their actions.
I'm someone who can't control their emotions.

For this . . .

I'm full of pain,
I'm full of shame.
Pain because of others,
Shame because of myself.

There's a lot of anger that burns within me,
Really, I don't know why.

The anger that's within me is caused by myself
Because I let my guard down
So my mind runs free,
My actions then take over.

For this I must be alone.
Alone to bear the pains,
Alone to see the shame.

I'm the kind of person that really should not be here.

Acacia Northe (13)
Cator Park School for Girls

Untitled

There are many different foods.
There are many foods to choose
But I just choose the foods
That I don't want to lose.

Food is sooo nice,
Right now I'm thinking about rice.
Really I'm thinking about the flavours,
The different tastes you get
When your mouth waters with joy,
Hmmmm! Reminds me of saveloy.

I come home from school,
I fell on my knees
And begged my mum to do
Macaroni and cheese.

I was sitting at the table,
My feet were kicking
But now I want
Some barbecue chicken.

Tammika West (14)
Cator Park School for Girls

Outcast

Outcast:
Do you know what that is?
Have you ever had that feeling
Because I have for a long time.

I'm not like you
Am I below average? Am I an Outcast?
I want to be like the others
Not to be the Outcast.
I have nothing and yet everyone has
Something.

I'm not a machine, I'm human
I have dreams too, just like you
Observe, Understand, Compare
Don't take short cuts.

Outcast:
I have grown up with this feeling
I presently have this feeling
And I have grown love for this feeling -
So leave me now to be my own
Outcast.

Hasinae Choudhury (16)
Cator Park School for Girls

A Night Out

Here I am, looking into the mirror,
Think, think, what to wear?
Should I have red or black,
Pink or white?
What will it be tonight?

I am all dressed for a night out
But I have to think, think,
What earrings to wear?
Should I have big or small,
Round or square?
What will it be tonight?

Almost done, one more thing to add.
Shoes, so think, think.
High or low, black or silver?
What will it be tonight?

Vuyo Kwitshana (14)
Cator Park School for Girls

A Wish

A wish is a dream you want to come true,
A wish is a dream that comes from you,
A wish is a feeling from inside,
A wish is a feeling you cannot hide,
A wish is something you cannot see,
A wish is something from you and me,
A wish is a chance for you to change,
A wish is a chance to start again.

Jade King (13)
Cator Park School for Girls

On A Sweet Day

How crisp the morn air,
Cold on my face,
Nipping at every inch of bare skin.
The radiant golden glow within me,
Growing with each step I take.
The grass crunching beneath me,
Snapping underneath my feet.
The wind blowing,
Wrapping round me like a ribbon,
Clouds, fluffy, wispy and light.
Pictures of faces, animals appear,
As if drawn in
By someone or something.
But yet here I am,
Standing alone,
Alone on a hill,
Staring at the sky on a sweet day.

Nisa Cooper (14)
Cator Park School for Girls

Love Is

Love is a red, red rose,
A box of chocolates sweeter than sugar,
A cloud slowly floating to Heaven,
It is a rainbow of happiness,
A deep river of overflowing red,
It is a sea of misty passion,
It separates us from who we are,
To who we are about to become,
It is our overhanging shadow,
Waiting to leap out.

Michael Parker (11)
Hugh Christie Technology College

Life As We Know It

Life as we know it
Is rubbish, we say,
We take it for granted
Every single day.

We want something new,
Our toys are now old,
This happens while a girl
Sits in the cold.

Her parents don't want her,
They've left her astray,
Alone in the darkness
Forever she'll lay.

A boy sits there crying,
His life crashing down,
Like an ever-flowing waterfall,
In a cold-hearted town.

A brother and sister,
Have only one pound,
And a blanket to warm them
While sitting on the ground.

So life as we know it,
Our luxuries, our homes,
Somebody would thank us
If our lives we could loan.

Madeleine Atkins (12)
Hugh Christie Technology College

Fireworks

Fireworks are scary,
Fireworks are fierce,
They pop, they crackle, they all go bang,
With amazing colours flying in all directions.

Luke Chatfield (11)
Hugh Christie Technology College

The Never-Ending Phone Call

There's a monster under my bed,
I know, *because*

He growls,
And prowls,
And scowls,
And howls.

He groans,
And moans,
And phones,

Who?
All the other monsters under beds.
Whooo.

Growl,
Prowl,
Scowl,
And howl.

Groan,
Moan,
And phone,

Who?
All the . . .

Tom Jones (11)
Hugh Christie Technology College

Storm

The wind is howling, the rain
Is lashing the windowpane
And the thunder is crashing.
I hate the storm.
I hate, hate, hate.
The storm is like WW2, all guns.
I hate the storm,
I hate, hate, hate.

Ben Rowswell (11)
Hugh Christie Technology College

If My Family Were Shoes

If my mum was a shoe,
She would be a slipper,
A purple, furry, soft slipper.
I wouldn't, would you?

If my dad was a shoe,
He would be a boot,
A big, smelly, old boot.
I wouldn't, would you?

If my sister was a shoe,
She would be a trainer,
A size 4, pure white trainer.
I wouldn't, would you?

If my brother was a shoe,
He would be a posh shoe,
A brown, shiny, posh shoe.
I wouldn't, would you?

Now if I were a shoe,
I would be a knee-high, black boot,
A nice, shiny, knee-high, black boot.
But how about you?

Joanne Wilson (11)
Hugh Christie Technology College

I Am

I am small as a newly planted tree.
My hair is bright like the sun.
I am thin as a twig.
I am sweet like a bun.

I am as cheeky as a monkey.
I am as nice as a pie.
I am as chatty as a letter box.
I am as thoughtful as a sigh.

Jasmine Thomson (11)
Hugh Christie Technology College

Summer . . .

Summer sweat
Skimming the beaches
Melting the lollies
Crushed each ice cube
And drank each drink
But not a move was made.

Summer lazed
On its burning towel
As it made the grass browner
Ripped each piece of skin
But not a move was made.

Summer gazed
Down the flowing stream
Catching each fly that whizzed by
On his arms were red flames
But not a move was made.

Georgia Van Ebeling (11)
Hugh Christie Technology College

Fireworks

The whizzing of the fireworks,
The whistle of the fireworks,
The bang of the fireworks,
The screaming of the fireworks,
The howling of the fireworks.

The crying of the children,
The screaming of the children,
The howling of the children.

The spit of the bonfire,
The popping of the bonfire,
The crunching of the bonfire.

The silence of the night.

Kayleigh Williamson (11)
Hugh Christie Technology College

There's A Monster In My Garden

There's a monster in my garden,
It's eating all the flowers.
There's a monster in my garden,
It's been there for hours.
There's a monster in my garden,
It's rolled up the path.
There's a monster in my garden,
I'm trying not to laugh.
There's a monster in my garden,
It's eaten the cat and dog.
There's a monster in my garden,
It's about to throw a log.
There's a monster in my garden,
I told my mum and dad.
There's a monster in my garden,
They said I was mad.

So if they don't believe me,
They'll be sorry, wait and see,
Cos *there's a monster in my garden*
And it isn't little old me.

Abbie White (12)
Hugh Christie Technology College

Visitor

A visitor is coming,
Quick, run to your seats,
The boys say she'll look stunning,
I wonder what she eats?

She wears red devil horns,
Apparently she fell in thorns,
Her black dress is horrible,
She used to be good at volleyball.

On class, let's get started?

Sophie Littlechild (11)
Hugh Christie Technology College

Louise

L is for her love light shining
O is only her
U is for understanding
I is for her importance
S is for her sensitivity
E is for her elegance.

Put them together to spell a name,
Lovely, longing, Louise.
Her eyes are like diamonds, all shiny and new,
Her lips are for kissing, especially for you,
Her cheeks are red like blooming roses,
Her nose is a button, but only you know this.

Her heart is wide open for you,
Because she loves you very much too.
Keep your chin up, you'll see her again,
Because her life has just begun.

Shannon Jenkins (12)
Hugh Christie Technology College

The Poem That I Made Up

The greatest car in the world is a Kenny racer,
With yellow lightning shocking down the side.
It won the competition as the sweet ride.
It bounces up an down like a kangaroo,
Its horn is like a noisy bird which goes coo, coo, coo.
It speeds down the road full Noz on,
In the night the roads are lit up with baby blue neon.
It's got huge speakers, when you put them on it hurts,
The Kenny racer has massive side skirts.
Inside it has a PS2,
Only for me and you.

Kenny Martin (11)
Hugh Christie Technology College

What Would It Be Like?

One morning I woke up and saw my mum standing over me, saying,

'What would it be like if there were no fizzy drinks?
What would it be like if the sun didn't exist?
What would it be like if as soon as you went to lick your ice cream
it melted?
What would it be like if there were no buildings and we all lived on
the streets?

What would it be like if there were no animals?
What would it be like if food was always cold?
What would it be like if food was always green?
What would it be like if there was no tea?'

The night has come and Mum has gone,
But what would it be like if I can't sleep?

Zoë Everest (11)
Hugh Christie Technology College

Wild Horses

The thundering hooves galloping across the hardened soil,
Their damp coats beginning to boil,
They were muzzling, nuzzling the scent of fear,
Their terrified neigh said fright was here.

They were running as fast as a racing car,
They had galloped so far,
Slowly round the corner wondering
What might be there.

Their eyes are white as snow,
Their hurdling, hurried legs beginning to slow,
The pack was coming to a stop,
Their worry had disappeared and now
They could eat until they went pop.

Rosie Try (11)
Hugh Christie Technology College

Shoes

If my mum was a shoe,
She would be a yellow high-heel,
Heavenly
All day long.

If my dad was a shoe,
He would be a black boot,
Building
All day long.

If my grandma was a shoe,
She would be a flip-flop,
Flipping and flopping
All day long.

If I was a shoe,
I would be a red and white trainer,
Training, skating,
All day long.

Peter Kilpatrick (11)
Hugh Christie Technology College

My Truck Poem

A truck has a windscreen and some windscreen wipers,
The engine roars like a tiger.
When it pulls a cargo container it goes vroom! Vroom!
In the container there was a Loch Ness monster,
Its head is so high, it breaks your neck
And you are in hospital.
And when you're in hospital, you will forget
What happened that day, about a truck.

Daniel Finn (11)
Hugh Christie Technology College

There's A Monster In My Bedroom

There's a monster in my bedroom
ripping all my clothes.
There's a monster in my bedroom,
everybody knows.

There's a monster in my bedroom,
rolling on my bed.
There's a monster in my bedroom,
pretending he is dead.

There's a monster in my bedroom,
what do I do?
There's a monster in my bedroom
screaming, 'Hippy, dippy, do.'

There's a monster in my bedroom,
I'm fed up now.
'Tea's ready.'

Holly James (12)
Hugh Christie Technology College

Monster Poem

His hair is as curly as pigs' tails,
His eyes are like red-hot fireballs,
His face has boils all over,
His tongue is tin foil,
His breath is like dog food,
His body is made out of a china doll,
His legs are china dolls,
His feet are made out of bins.

Zoë Pennells (11)
Hugh Christie Technology College

If My Family Was A Shoe

If my mum was a shoe,
She would be a slipper,
A pink, fluffy, soft slipper,
What about you?

If my dad was a shoe,
He would be a boot,
A black, dirty, smelly boot.
What about you?

If my brother was a shoe,
He would be a trainer,
A blue, muddy, cheesy trainer.
What about you?

If my sister was a shoe,
She would be a posh shoe,
A black, high-heeled shoe.
What about you?

Now if I was a shoe,
I would be bare,
My own bare, dirty, smelly feet.
What about you?

Keighley Kucers (11)
Hugh Christie Technology College

Football

Football is a wonderful game,
It can cause good or cause some pain.
It is my favourite sport to play,
I could play all night and day.
The managers screaming, the coaches roar,
The players run, they want to score.
The whistle blows for a horrible foul,
The players give a nasty scowl.
If you win the game it can be great,
But losing games I really hate.

Sam Hasler (11)
Hugh Christie Technology College

Summer!

Summer stomped
Through the shimmering desert,
Scorching sand,
Squashed each bug and crinkled each cactus,
The heat of the sun from his hand.

Summer trekked
Up the groaning mountain,
Every footpath scarred and burnt,
Rivers dry, mud banks crack,
Lessons of the heatwave now truly learnt.

Summer sprinted
Up the dusty creek,
Lizards sunbathing by the shrinking pond,
Butterfly settling upon a rose,
Summers to remember as friendships bond.

Jemma Dunville (11)
Hugh Christie Technology College

There's A Monster In My Garden

There's a monster in my garden,
I went to my mother,
Who told me not to bother,
It might be my imagination.
So I ran to the station.
It ate my brother,
I thought it was another,
I went to my dad,
Who told me I was mad.
I told my sister,
She was busy with a blister!

There's a monster in my garden,
May I tell you? Because you can tell me
What to do.

Grant Stonehouse (11)
Hugh Christie Technology College

Ferrari

I am a Ferrari, long and slick,
My many shapes and sizes, take your pick.
I am the fastest thing on four wheels,
But with me also come a few bills.

My dad is a V12 engine,
He is the main part of me,
He always keeps me going,
And he buzzes like a bee.

My mum is the air-conditioning,
She keeps me warm and cold,
And if we have a small crash,
She will stay strong and bold.

Matthew J Smith (12)
Hugh Christie Technology College

Half Term

Half term's cool,
Half term's great,
Have a lay in,
Through half-past eight.

You can go to the park
And play football,
And at the weekend
Go to the swimming pool.

Don't worry about homework,
There's none to do,
But there's probably a piece
In your bag for you.

Jake Fairweather (11)
Hugh Christie Technology College

War

As we saw
The enemy was raw
We began to look
I readied my hook

As we charged
The enemy was large
We began to fight
Then it turned to night

I thought they would yield
My weapon I wield
The battle was fierce
My sword would pierce

The enemy retreats
So we follow and they bleat
Blood on the floor
The end of the war.

Thomas Prior (11)
Hugh Christie Technology College

Autumn

Autumn has arrived,
The trees look bare,
The rustling brown leaves
Blow here and there.

Cut up your pumpkins,
Trick or treat,
Turn on the heating,
Warm your feet.

The conkers are ready,
The cold winds blow,
Put on my woolly jumper,
I can't wait for the snow.

Cortney Osborne (11)
Hugh Christie Technology College

Potion Shop

Hey yey want to a buy a potion?
We make all kinds, no commotion,
We'll make a potion just for you
Even when we've got the flu
All the spices, hey let's have some of that
(rappa tap tap)
That must be them, I'll open the door
Nearly ready dears we'll just add . . .
A shrieking skull
A cow's tail
A lot of snow
An old man's beard
Eye of newt
Sweaty arm hair
Lizard's ear wax
And shrivelled brains
Now just a lick of heat.

Here you go please enjoy.

Max Maton (11)
Hugh Christie Technology College

Fireworks

Whee goes the rocket as it shoots up in the sky,
Crackle goes the sparklers in my hand,
Whoosh, the Catherine wheel spins around and around,
Screech goes the fireworks, straight above our heads,
Banging, popping noises fill our ears,
Melting, dripping guy burning on the roaring fire,
Bang! An explosion of colours up high,
Clap, clap, clap, the children laugh and cheer.

Rebecca Broad (11)
Hugh Christie Technology College

Cricket

Pull out your cricket bat,
You're up next,
Defending the ball,
With special effects.

Get ready to bowl,
Bowling with pace,
Don't let the team down,
Remember it's not a race.

Wicket keeping is the best,
Stopping the extras, catching the ball,
Diving to the left, to the right,
Keeping ball in hand, hope it won't fall.

Ben Turner (11)
Hugh Christie Technology College

Christmas

Christmas Day is coming soon,
Make sure you are asleep at midnight's moon.
It is over for Christmas Eve,
Santa Claus is about to leave.

Quick, wake up, look in your stocking,
Look, one present is rocking.
Rush downstairs and have your brekkie,
Give a present to your friend Becky.

Look! Christmas dinner is here,
Eat the tasty turkey and hurry up because . . .
It's almost a happy new year!

Emily Hazell (11)
Hugh Christie Technology College

If The World Was Made Out Of Chocolate

What a wonderful world it would be,
the cloud, the sun, the countryside,
The river, the beach and the sea.

The houses, the cars, the buses,
The bicycles, the pushchairs and skates,

The kettle, the saucepan, and dustbin,
The cups, the saucers and plates.

The cats, the dogs, the tortoises,
The guinea pigs, the rabbits and mice.

If the world was made out of chocolate,
What a wonderful world it would be.

Zoe Chatfield (11)
Hugh Christie Technology College

Fireworks Night

Do you see on fireworks night,
The way that dogs get a terrible fright,
When the fireworks go up in the air,
Some people get a very big scare.

Fireworks go up with a very big bang,
Men doing a play, the swords go clang,
When the fireworks go up in the air,
Some people get a very big scare.

So when you go to fireworks night,
Remember you're in for a very big fright,
Remember why you are actually there,
Remember you're in for a very big scare.

Hayley Tompson (11)
Hugh Christie Technology College

My Favourite Thing

My favourite thing is as cuddly
As a teddy bear,
As sneaky as a spy,
It's sweet as sherbet,
And as soft as a piece of silk,
My wonderful thing is as lazy as a snail,
As daft as a monkey,
It's as little as a baby's finger and
As light as a feather.
My funny thing is as smily as a clown,
As kind as a nurse,
And annoying as brothers.
My cool thing is as cute as a puppy,
As nice as a sweet, and as furry as cotton wool.

Katie Harris (11)
Hugh Christie Technology College

Hallowe'en

Hallowe'en makes me scream,
Witches, ghouls and ghosts,
Going round eating sweets,
See who's sick the most.

Pumpkins, bats, spiders and owls,
High-pitched screams and horrible howls,
People in costumes, it is dark
There are lots of scary masks.

Spooky, scary, creepy, boo,
Yuck, I trod in some sticky goo,
Lanterns, torches in the dark,
We're going out trick or treating!

Joannah Roots (11)
Hugh Christie Technology College

My Dog

My dog Tessa
Is very old,
Like a castle
On a tall hill.

She is a German Shepherd,
Her fur is very dark,
As a storm
In the sky.

She howls at the phone,
She loves to chew at her bone,
But she is a big softy.

Natalie Gillham (11)
Hugh Christie Technology College

What Is . . . A Cloud?

A cloud is a fluffy pile of feathers,
Floating gently through the sky.

A cloud is a sheep fleece,
Hanging in the sky.

A cloud is a cotton wool,
Gracefully going by.

A cloud is an icy kiss,
Frozen in the sky.

A cloud is smoke,
Lingering in the sky.

Danielle Standen (12)
Hugh Christie Technology College

My Game

Football is the thing I like,
You can't compare with riding a bike.
Scoring a goal makes me feel fantastic,
My mum and my nan say, 'Your legs are elastic!'
My dad's on the sideline, shouting out loud,
My mum's really cheering, looking real proud.
The pitch is my freedom,
The ball is my joy,
Winning is pleasure,
I'm a happy boy.

Alexander Hughesman (11)
Hugh Christie Technology College

Football

Try and score a goal,
Hope it doesn't hit the football pole.
Pass the ball,
Don't fall.

Save the ball that's coming at you like a bullet,
Don't overdo it.
So play really well
And it does ring a bell.

Jackson Harris (12)
Hugh Christie Technology College

The Spider

S mall I am and small I'll be,
P eople don't much care for me.
I hang on the ceiling and the wall,
D efying death if you're tall.
E veryone I'd keep away,
R ecognise me, I'm here to stay.

Ben Payne (11)
Hugh Christie Technology College

My Favourite Person

My favourite person is as kind as a mother hen,
As beautiful as a model,
They're as elegant as a dancer,
And wonderful like a mum should be.

My favourite person is like candyfloss,
Is sweet as chocolate,
They're friendly like a new dog,
And they're as shimmering as the distant stars.

My favourite person is as sweet as a rose,
They're like a loving dolphin,
As quiet as a spider crawling up your back,
And as soft as a baby duckling.

My favourite person is as bubbly as a brook,
They're as funny as a clown,
As clever as a scientist,
And like a heroine in my eyes!

Chloé Shrubsole (12)
Hugh Christie Technology College

The Nightmare Monkeys

I cast this spell to kill you
Eye of newt and monkey too,
Guess what I'm going to kill you!
So be aware the monkey's scare!

I cast this spell to kill you,
Lace of boot and eye of you,
Guess what I'm going to kill you,
Arm them with axes and shields too!
So be aware the monkey's scare!

Liam Foster (12)
Hugh Christie Technology College

Bullying

I want to die,
Watching the time slowly go by,
I walked into school,
Thinking this isn't cool,
My feelings were sad,
I feel so bad,
I needed to escape this life,
I wanted to cut myself with a knife,
I ran into the loos,
Not knowing what to do,
My life was in shatters,
All bruised and battered,
My life was hell,
I hate those girls,
Why do they have to pick on me,
The tears scream down my face,
Why do I feel so out of place?
One day, one day
The pain will go away,
Please just help me.

Emily Charman (12)
Hugh Christie Technology College

The Witch's Spell

I cast this spell to wake the dead,
Human eyes and heart still beating,
Bony vomit from a dog,
Stirring these up to make the potion,
In a jar from the donkey's nation.

For this spell will wake the dead,
In this poem there will be dread,
And on this potion, you will be fed,
In the everlasting dread.

Stephen Connor (11)
Hugh Christie Technology College

The Witch's Spell

I cast this spell to create Hell,
Rotten heart and bearded shark,
Slimy mud and manky blood,
Revolting eye and Satan's lie,
Blackened tooth and killing booth,
All these things go in the pot,
So it will rot,
Echoing bang and pirate's slang,
Gunman's pistol and shiny crystal,
Armpit hairs and shrunken plum and thumb,
Skanky fungus and stomach bugs,
All these things go in the pot,
So it will rot.

Ben James (11)
Hugh Christie Technology College

The Witch's Spells

I cast this spell to make people come back from the dead,
I throw in some oozing eyeballs,
I mush in some rotten bogies,
I break up a horrible skeleton,
I splattered some mouldy intestines,
I am pouring in stinky vinegar,
I am adding in old cat legs,
I am stirring in some manky mud,
I am putting in some stinky poo,
I am dropping in some manky hair,
I am dropping in some old stories,
I am breaking up some mouldy bananas.

Luke Powell (12)
Hugh Christie Technology College

The Witch's Spell

I cast this spell to wake the dead,
Mouldy liver and rotten apples,
Foul vomit and bloody squid,
Slimy eel skin and shrivelled fungus,
Manky rabbit eyes and spurting chicken's head,
Squidgy earwax and sticky mud,
Bony goat and rotting flesh,
Rancid manure and human heart,
Gutty fish and gross snot,
Skanky snake and spurting veins,
Maggoty bread and gone off cheese.

Sam Chesson (11)
Hugh Christie Technology College

The Witch's Spell

I cast this spell to wake the dead:

Through the snake's head
Which has been brewed,
Add a bit of oxtail stew,
And some mixed herbs,
An eye of a shark.

Mixing it with a giant spoon,
Holding ingredients in their hands,
Pots surrounding the witch's cauldron,
Wearing mouldy aprons and green hands.

Brett Wallis (11)
Hugh Christie Technology College

My Favourite Thing

My favourite thing is as soppy as a baby,
As cuddly as a bear,
It's playful like a child,
And as soft like a kitten.

My dog is as loud as a lion,
As heavy as a hippo,
It's big like an elephant,
And it's smooth like a feather.

My dog is as loveable as me,
And as sweet as can be,
He's handsome like a prince,
And is cute like a lamb.

My dog is as greedy as a hippo,
As funny as a clown,
He's hairy like a gorilla,
And is as best as can be.

Emma Broom (11)
Hugh Christie Technology College

My Goldfish

My first goldfish, Goldie,
Is as scaly as a lizard,
As shiny as a new car,
As gold as the sun,
And as hungry as a dog.

My other goldfish, Darkness,
Is as fast as a hawk,
As dark as the night,
As sneaky as a spy,
And as quiet as a mouse.

Joshua Dalby (11)
Hugh Christie Technology College

My Favourite Thing

My favourite person is as lovely as TV,
As stupid as a bag,
It is funny like a kangaroo
And beautiful like my mum.

My favourite thing is as quiet as a teddy,
As fast as a car,
It is stupid like a frog,
And as handsome like me.

My favourite person is as kind as a toy,
As brilliant as a calculator,
It is as brightly coloured like a peach,
And shaky like a table.

My favourite thing is as slow as a tortoise,
As sneaky as a monkey,
It is colourful like a rainbow,
And as jumpy like a rabbit.

Tommy Smith (11)
Hugh Christie Technology College

Death

I cast this spell to wake the dead . . .

Slugs and snails with puppy dog tails,
Heart and lungs with an ox's tongue,
Chewing gum from a tramp's bum,
Heart and whale with foul toe nails,
Eye of newt and monkey too,
Guess what? I'm going to kill you,
A dash of poo will kill you,
Be aware this monkey's scare!

Perry Smith (11)
Hugh Christie Technology College

The Witch's Spell

I cast this spell to kill James Bond,
Take some rotten intestines,
Boiling bogies . . .

Sticky skeletons,
Bloody bodies,
Elephant ears,
Sprinkle in,
Tiger toes,
Lions legs,
Rotten intestines,
Spongy spot,
Mouldy foot,
Brain of a newt,
Bats' wings,
Dog's tail.

Michael Fox (11)
Hugh Christie Technology College

The Witch's Spell

I cast this spell to make people
Come back from the dead
Oozing eyeballs
A pinch of rotten bogies,
Horrific skeleton
Bloody carcass
Sprinkle in some mouldy intestines
Stinky vinegar
Bushy frogs' legs
Minging hairs
Hairy legs
And add some manky mud *and stir!*

Reece Huggins (12)
Hugh Christie Technology College

The Dragon Of Death

In a faraway, faraway land,
Lies a treasure of infinite,
But guarding it closely forever,
Looms a being as old as the Earth,
It's body is big as a boulder,
And armoured with shimming scales,
Even the mountain tops tremble,
When it thrashes its seven great tails.

The dragon of death is its name.

Alex Richardson (11)
Hugh Christie Technology College

I Am

I am as short as an elf,
I am as hard as stone,
I am as thin as a stick,
I am as blonde as the sun,
I am as fast as a cheetah,
My hair is as spiky as a hedgehog,
I am as fun as a lion.

Liam Palmer (12)
Hugh Christie Technology College

Seven Heads

Seven heads
Gleam with a red flame
Teeth sharper than daggers
As old as the Earth
Big as a boulder
Seven great tails
Shimmering scales.

Lauren Claire Gillham (11)
Hugh Christie Technology College

Similes Poem

My object is light as pasta,
My object is as crunchy as a crisp,
My object is a bendy as a paper,
As light as a feather,
As quiet as a mouse,
As noisy as lions,
As heavy as a sword,
As bad as a film,
As boring as a book.

Leian Davies (11)
Hugh Christie Technology College

Dead Ringers

I cast a spell to wake the dead,
And kill the living.

A toad's eye,
A cat's leg,
Frog's head,
Mouldy corpses
And human blood.
Beware you're in for a scare!

Jack Reynolds-Wooding (11)
Hugh Christie Technology College

Matthew!

Matthew is a wicked bloke,
Who's everybody's mate,
He's really smooth,
He's in the groove,
He's funky and he's great!

Matthew Martin (11)
Hugh Christie Technology College

The Money Poem

Slices of snails,
With puppy dog's tail,
Slithers of rat,
And eye of bat,
Legs of frogs,
And tusks of hogs,
Bring it to the boil and let it bubble,
Or you will be in for trouble.

Add the tail of a cat,
And felt from a witch's hat,
Drain the warm stew,
And take a sip from the brew,
Add a £1 note
And watch it float,
Add a pinch of fish,
We've finished the dish.

Hubble, bubble, boil and trouble,
Fires burn, cauldrons bubble,
Let it chill with snake tongue,
To ensure your spell is done.

Joshua Haslam (11)
Hugh Christie Technology College

PE

PE is so cool,
It keeps you really fit
Do your athletics,
That way you will be really quick.

Go on be an Olympic champ,
Before you get too old,
Make Britain proud,
Now bring back gold.

Ben Tyler (11)
Hugh Christie Technology College

Revolting Recipe

I cast a spell to Miss Lockett,
First witch, you need a pot and spoon,
Second witch, you need some ingredients,
Third witch, then you mix it together,
Fourth witch, start to say what the ingredients are,
Fifth witch, coughing chillers oozing out,
Murky mint sauce, boring bubble bath,
Crumbly cheese, prickly pasta,
Second witch, then you need to mix it all
But you will need a big bowl and a big spoon,
You put a little bit of water in,
Third witch, then you put it in the pot,
And shake it about, then stir it,
Fourth witch, then you take it in but
Always put in a carrier bag.

Kayleigh Powell (11)
Hugh Christie Technology College

Football

My favourite thing is as freaky as Friday,
As fun as a circus,
It is as brilliant as a holiday,
It is as funny as dawn,
The ball is as round as the sun,
A kit is like a uniform,
Our boots sound like horses in a stable,
Our shin pads are as hard as wood,
A pitch is like a well-kept field,
The goal is like a mouth of a cave,
The linesmen are like yo-yo's,
The referee is like a boss.

Ryan Walmsley (12)
Hugh Christie Technology College

My Favourite Person

My favourite person is as cuddly as a teddy bear,
As sweet as a kitten,
As caring as a Care Bear.

My favourite person is as cheeky as a monkey,
As muscely as Popeye,
He really is funky.

My favourite person is really great,
My favourite person is my brother Jake.

Lisa Rogers (11)
Hugh Christie Technology College

Storm

The howling of the wind as it comes through the chimney,
The crashing as the trees fall to the ground,
The rumble of the ground as the lightning hits the floor,
The dogs as they woof into the sky in a mad rage,
The banging of the houses as they fall and crumble to the ground,
The screeching of the cars as they break in a mad rush,
The pattering of the raindrops as they fall onto the window,
The whistling of the wind as the fierce storm calms.

Jasmine Sutton (11)
Hugh Christie Technology College

Fireworks Night

The boom of the banger,
The screech of the banshee,
The fizz of the Roman candle,
The crackle of the Catherine wheel,
The swish of the rocket,
The booming in the air.

Luke South (11)
Hugh Christie Technology College

Bat Poem

Bats fly through the night sky,
Bats so black you can't see them,
Bats fly through the trees and caves,
Soundless in the night,
So don't go out on bat night,
You might not be able to
See them but they're coming
For you now!

Dean Bradley (12)
Hugh Christie Technology College

Bonfire Night

On the 5th of November, this is what you hear,
The cheering of the people,
The whistling of the fireworks,
The bang of the flame,
The crackle of the sparklers,
The scattering of the fireworks,
Then the pop of the bonfire.

Katie Brown (11)
Hugh Christie Technology College

Diggers

A digger can go anywhere,
A digger can lift anything,
It wants to lift,
A digger can dig holes so deep,
A digger can go over anything because of
Its powerful engine,
A digger can roar really loud.

Jay Nash (11)
Hugh Christie Technology College

Fireworks

High up in the sky,
All fireworks fly,
Pink, white and green,
Better than I've ever seen.

Twirling, crackling, sparkling too,
Bang, bang, bang,
Boom, boom, boom.

They look so good,
They are so bright,
Fireworks are the best,
When used at night.

Kerry Smith (12)
Hugh Christie Technology College

Dead Ringers

I cast a spell to wake the dead,
And kill the living,
A splurge of blood,
And a manky eyeball,
And a manky corpse,
Bloody faces,
A steer of oozing bodies,
A pinch of hair falling out potion,
A jug of human saliva,
A blob of human blood,
And a crucified cow,
A pinch of blubbering, boiled, bloody bugs.

Ross Kent (12)
Hugh Christie Technology College

Please Miss Parsons

'Please Miss Parsons
This girl Laura Asplin
Keeps pulling my hair Miss,
What shall I do?'

'Go tell Mr Sheppard dear,
Go home and hide,
Take your book and sit with Mr O'Docherty, my lamb
Do what you want . . . '

'Please Miss Parsons,
This girl Laura Asplin
Keeps kicking me Miss
What shall I do?'

'Kick her back dear,
Lock yourself in the cupboard,
Sit with your friends my love,
Do what you think best?'

'Please Miss Parsons
This girl Laura Asplin
Keeps calling me rude names Miss
What shall I do?'

'Hit yourself over the head lamb,
Run to Tunbridge Wells,
Do whatever you can my flower.

But don't ask me!'

Sheree Pennells (13)
Hugh Christie Technology College

Storm

The crashing of the thunder,
The crackling of the lightning,
The creaking of the tree,
The howling of the wind.

The dripping of the rain,
The swoshing of the tide,
The banging of the shutters,
The flickering of the lights.

The whistling of the wind,
The hissing of the rain,
The creaking of the doors,
The snapping of the branch.

And the rain was lashing
The windowpane.

Lewis Beacham (11)
Hugh Christie Technology College

My Spell

Tooth of a dragon and tongue of snake,
Mix together with a big rake,
Wolfman's leg and vampire bat,
And toe nails of a large rat,
Dead bats' wings and power sphere,
We are so close we are near,
Frankenstein's bolts and mummy's robe,
Mix together with an earlobe,
Lightning bolt and thunder clash,
Now I've got a really big rash,
Giant frog and tail of dog,
Mix together in a bog.

Sharni Daniel Chapman (12)
Hugh Christie Technology College

The Storm

The wind did whirl around the trees,
And howled like a Jupiterian breeze,
Branches cracking in the wind,
Spears of rain bounced off the ground.

Like a horde of screaming banshees,
The storm roared in from the east,
And slammed the doors and windows loudly,
Under black and looming clouds.

James Workman (11)
Hugh Christie Technology College

The Storm

The rumble of the thunder,
The pelting of the rain,
The honk of a car,
The howling of the wind.

The crackle of lightning,
The sizzling of telephone wires,
The crack of a tree,
The sound of a storm.

Tom Carter (11)
Hugh Christie Technology College

The Moon

The moon is a golden coin glittering in the night sky,
The moon is like a sun all golden and beautiful as a rose,
The moon is a ball of cheese,
The moon is a doughnut all golden and crispy,
The moon is a cake all covered with icing,
And tastes like a toffee ice cream cone.

Marian Hinchliffe (11)
Hugh Christie Technology College

Snow

Snow is white glitter that falls from the sky,
When it snows everything goes quiet,
Snowflakes are fluffy and light,
Landing on trees and cars that are in its path.

Snow is a white blanket,
That covers over the land,
Crunching when you walk on it,
Pulling your coat together to keep you warm.

Snow is a slush puppy,
Melting in the sun,
Now it is a brown mess,
That makes a mess indoors.

Danielle Hayward (11)
Hugh Christie Technology College

Bonfire Night

On Bonfire Night hear
The whoosh of the rocket,
As it shoots up into the air,
The screaming of the screamers,
And the crackling of the sparklers.

On Bonfire Night hear
The popping of the bonfire,
But soon all will die down,
People will go home,
And Bonfire Night will be no more.

Samantha Hedges (12)
Hugh Christie Technology College

Metaphor Poem About Cassi My Dog

Cassi is a monkey,
Because she's silly and funny,
She is a pre-wash,
To take care of left-overs,
Before the dishwasher,
Sometimes she's a race car,
Just due to her speed,
She's a leader,
Never left behind,
And sometimes she's a robot,
Only made to play!

Kjell Folkesson (11)
Hugh Christie Technology College

Animals

Slithering snakes, slimy and slow - don't make a sound,
Tiny turtle trotters towards the tide - never to be found,
Hungry hamster hurries over hurdles to hide away,
Lippy, leaning lizards running up the wall,
And a rat may not be your best friend,
But they're still quite cool.
Eager, energetic eagle, expert at hunting food,
Cheating cheetah as fast as a rocket,
Rabbits hopping in and out of burrows,
Hyper hyena can't stop laughing,
Mischievous monkey counts his money -
He's got the most, the other animals don't think it's funny.

Ellie Barton (11)
Hugh Christie Technology College

Fireworks

Fireworks go crash,
Fireworks go wheeee,
Fireworks go smash,
In front of you and me.

Fireworks go clang,
Fireworks go wheeee,
Fireworks go bang!
In front of you and me.

Gary Clark (12)
Hugh Christie Technology College

Love

Love is a special thing to have,
Love is a special thing to share,
Love is about caring and being together,
Love is being together forever and always,
Love is a special thing,
So why waste it?

Shannon Bishop (11)
Hugh Christie Technology College

PE

Jogging round the sports hall,
Running on the pitch,
Doing hop, skip and jump,
Till I get a stitch.

Running like an antelope,
Jumping like a deer,
Clashing our hockey sticks,
Oh dear, oh dear!

Ellie Jones (11)
Hugh Christie Technology College

Detention

Clamber into the brown old room,
I'm given an evil stare,
Crawl to the empty chair and sit,
It was only a stupid dare.

Scribble and write down all the work,
Watching the flock freeze,
I'm stutting and stopping, it's stuffy in here,
If only there was a breeze.

Come to the bad bit, I want to lie,
Or should I just tell it all?
The dare was so stupid; I shouldn't have done it,
To think it wasn't funny at all.

Walk out of school feeling ashamed,
Walking down the street,
Bag feeling heavy, I'm dragging it home,
I'm staring down at my feet.

Come to a hill; I'm gazing high up,
Start to wander home,
Dazed and forget where I'm going,
End up being alone.

I'm in an alley, starts to get dark,
I hear a strange noise,
Is someone there or am I dreaming?
There! I see some boys!

They turn and run after me,
Freeze, start to run,
It's black now, I start to see some lights,
Run, it's not fun.

Suddenly I'm surrounded by lights,
Glaring all in my eyes,
Pray to God, this is the end,
I'm sorry for all my lies.

It hurt at first in my leg,
Then the screeching attack,
Saw the blackness of the tyre,
That's all . . . it goes black . . .

Kieran Mulholland (13)
Langley Park School for Boys

Detention

Sitting in the room alone,
Writing many lines,
Teacher sitting at her desk,
Waiting to give the sign.

All because I was talking,
In class today,
All going well and good,
Then she made me stay.

She told me she caught me talking,
And shouted for a bit,
I ignored what she was saying,
Then she went into a fit.

Up we went to the headmaster's room,
He stood there watching me,
I stared right back into his eyes,
As far as I could see.

He asked why I was standing there?
Shaking, I stayed silent,
He kept on staring very had,
In the detention, head bent.

Sitting in the stuffy room,
What had I done?
Sitting in the stuffy room,
It certainly wasn't fun!

Giuseppe Scannapieco (13)
Langley Park School for Boys

The Detention

Shaking, I enter the classroom doorway,
Knowing it hasn't been done,
'Homework out on desks please boys,'
My head starts to drum.

As the teacher walks past everyone's desk,
With a smile on her face she passes,
The second she passes my empty desk,
She thinks she needs her glasses.

'No homework for Sloane I see on your desk,'
'Sorry Miss,' I try to explain,
No explanation comes out of my mouth,
There is no one else to blame.

'I left it on the kitchen shelf,'
I try to explain again,
She doesn't take any lame excuses,
Now sixty minutes of pain.

Three o'clock comes the next afternoon,
The bell rings after fifth class,
Walking through the crowded hallway,
'Excuse me, I have to get past.'

In detention I waited for almost an hour,
The minutes pass ever slower,
One more line of lines to write,
My pencil lead is getting lower.

I look at the clock again, again,
The bell still hasn't rung,
The punishment hasn't been too bad,
My bag over my shoulder is slung.

Abel Sloane (13)
Langley Park School for Boys

Detention

I'm just walking on my way to school,
Can't get it off my mind,
Hate this teacher, she picks on me,
She is not at all kind!

I know I have a detention in store,
I could bunk and run away,
But I'm not like that at all,
Because I like to face every day.

Oh that stupid homework has got me in trouble!
What will it be today?
Questions buzzing through my mind like a hive,
Now my stomach isn't feeling OK.

Entering the gates like an innocent Year 7
Nerves, nerves from this useless homework,
In the lesson the teacher asks for the work,
Mouths open, no words come out.

'Official!' she shouts out, not surprising me,
Handing me the yellow slip,
I'm the odd one out in the class with no homework,
Lonely, I bite my lip.

Now I am paying for what I have done,
Watching time pass by,
Slowly the hands move round the clock,
I wish the time would fly.

Alex Gil (13)
Langley Park School for Boys

The Detention

Walking to the detention room,
Thinking what have I done?
All I did was throw a rubber,
It was kinda fun.

I walked into the empty classroom,
The teacher was sitting there,
Stood up and shouted 'You're late!'
'I was talking to Miss Hair.'

'Whatever boy, now take your lines,
One hundred will do!'
'*Argh!* That can't be fair!'
'Be quiet or I will make you do two.'

'There you go, finished them sir,'
'OK now get out.'
I walked out the gate and on my way home,
The det was unfair without a doubt.

I was jogging home, then it started to rain,
My hair went wet and flat,
It was hard to see, my vision was blurred,
Wish I possessed some sort of hat!

I got to the corner of my road,
I started to run and almost did stack,
From the Heaven's above there was a big, white blast,
And everything just went black . . .

Jack Jastrzebski (13)
Langley Park School for Boys

Space

Space, the void of nothing, of solitude,
An eternity of glittering dots,
An endless archive of all things,
Each and every insignificant dot a book,
Each with its own unique saga,
Never touched, sitting unused, upon the black shelves,
Receding into nothing,
All watching patiently,
Watching, waiting with deadly patience,
Each one of these timid specks just the cover to the story,
A story that burns with fury and loneliness,
Radiating incandescent beauty,
Whispering tales of gargantuan red giants, sinister black holes,
Of gas clouds of stunning beauty and proportions,
Of the small flower of life,
The single flower of life,
The single thing we know,
Just one letter, in one word, in one sentence,
In one paragraph, in one book, in one small universe.

Thomas Moynihan (12)
Langley Park School for Boys

Captured

The result of an unwanted incident,
A terrible product of war.
A group of men offering their services,
To help rebuild a city and the law.

Fears of a dreadful death,
Like the slaughtering of cattle
The evil, capped man swipes the heads of innocents without a breath,
Clamping the chains without a rattle,
And quickly being put to death.

Sharif Elsabagh (13)
Langley Park School for Boys

Detention

Here I am, back again,
In the detention room,
Writing line upon line upon line,
With a sense of impending doom.

Why did I throw that stupid rubber?
It was not worth this pain!
And why did it have to hit stupid Matthew?
Who grassed me up again.

I went and said I was sorry to Matthew,
I pressed a fiver into his hand,
He slipped the money into his pocket
And turned around and ran.

I look up at the clock on the wall,
As it drags the second hand round,
I'd give anything to be at home on the computer,
Or outside playing around.

Must have been here for at least an hour,
Or maybe a bit more,
My head sinks down onto the desk,
And I start to snore.

Must have slept for ages and ages,
Now imagine my fright,
When I look up and see that yellow slip,
That says, 'Detention tomorrow night.'

Linden Lonsdale (13)
Langley Park School for Boys

The Destruction Of The Rainforest

The animals move swiftly with great agility,
Some higher up swinging through the trees,
Screams from young ones looking for their parent's protection,
What could this horrid monster that scares the rainforest be?

Entanglements of roots slowing down the hurry,
The smaller animals sense it and so starts the scurry,
No time to stop and eat, the consequences severe,
As here comes the machines attacking from the rear.

No tripping, no slowing, a mental sign appears,
Protesters watch on with faces full of tears,
Fitness vital for the animals to escape,
The machines drone on, what a mistake!

The rusty machine extinguishes the sorry land,
Homes obliterated to pieces no greater than your hand,
The metallic monsters groaning with virtual pain,
But nothing compares to the devastation they've caused today.

It's comforting to know it will all end soon,
As the monkeys cry, howling to the moon,
The workers see the havoc they've made,
Is it really worth it for what they're paid?

Business, profits, progress, what do all the animals gain?
They lose their homes, some lose their lives,
All they gain is pain.

Robert Gillow (12)
Langley Park School for Boys

The Sea

It just lies silently waiting to pounce,
Purring every now and then,
When a soft wave climbs up the shore,
Waiting for its perfect time to strike,
Slowly, it picks itself off the cold, breathless land far below,
The waves grow three inches each time,
Gradually building up to its climax.

The rocks on the shore sink slowly below the water,
The waves keep coming like a dog's paw,
Rising, then sinking back, building up to release a burst of energy,
Crushing anything in its vast path,
Then the beast stands to unleash its tremendous force,
It crashes down, sending great ripples across the shore,
It repeats itself several times on the beat of thunder.

Slowly it dies down three inches at a time,
Till it lies snoring across the deep seabed.

Ben McClymont (12)
Langley Park School for Boys

Imagine . . .

Imagine a place
Where darkness covers all,
Small voices in the rubble plead
And innocent men fall.
Imagine the girl
Who hears her brother cry,
Helicopters swooping low,
Her friend lies down to die.

Imagine the bone
Protruding from her knee,
As clinging to her faith,
She cries out desperately.

'There is no Allah but Allah!
There is no Allah but Allah!'

Michael Glover (14)
Langley Park School for Boys

Russian School Siege

Second of September, Beslan's Middle School Number One,
The children were playing and having fun.
Parents carrying flowers and teachers in their best
Not knowing that in three days, two hundred would come to rest.

Masked men quickly crossed the railway track,
Children ran towards them, anxious parents waved them back.
Under gun point they were forced into the gym
They all feared that the outcome would be grim!

No food or water, and as hot as Hell!
From fear and exhaustion many fell.
The huge explosion caused metal and glass to descend,
Escape was all that mattered, they just wanted it to end.

They ran past corpses starting to rot
As they did so, some were shot
The lucky survivors will never forget
The worst Chechen rebel attack yet!

Bevan Freake (13)
Langley Park School for Boys

The Hunt

Oh, how fun it must be,
For all those men, hounds and horses,
To watch the scared foxes run and flee,
Chased all over the courses.

At least the government voted for a ban,
But people protested, stood and fought.
Some broke into the Commons, what a plan,
But in the end at least they got caught.

Oh, how fun it must be,
For all those men, hounds and horses,
To watch the scared foxes run and flee,
Then ripped apart on the courses.

Adam Smith (13)
Langley Park School for Boys

School Of Horrors

Start of school, hated by many Beslan children,
But none knew of the horrors to come.
Tranquillity, silence, peace, for now the quieted,
Children work rigorously, then it begun.

There was a siege! Panic . . . Confusion . . . Anarchy!
Chechen terrorists stormed the school.
Horrific, masked terrors appearing suddenly,
Taking hostages, children, adults so cruel.

Lead helplessly towards the gym,
Scared, terrified, not understanding why.
The terrorists add more to their list of sin,
Planting mines across the school to die.

Many shaken children flee,
While captors shoot them down.
Images infants should not see,
Bloody corpses across the ground.

Days fixed in hellish captivity,
Without food or water, trapped . . . terrified.
Boom! The gym collapses, dreaded by the city,
Many children massacred beneath and died.

Seconds later children flee in fright,
The youngest were too scared to run.
Blood shod and the weak hobble into sight,
A shock-stricken parent looks for his son.

Security forces move in to help,
Nothing but carcasses line the floor.
Gun battles go on without a yelp,
Children appearing more and more.

The troops finally have control,
Only a few terrorists left now.
Barricaded in the basement full of coal,
Including the leader who must take a final bow.

The horrors will live on for years,
Being remembered for the innocent deaths.
But it will never heal the tears,
Of all those final dying breaths.

Nick Clegg (13)
Langley Park School for Boys

Contagion

It spreads like a falling domino
Taking every other new victim with it.
A chain reaction,
Like a bullied child
The victim gets singled out by the frightened crowd,
It comes as a shock and soon it totally engulfs the victim,
The infected are weak, paralysed with sickness,
Deadly germs career through your bloodstream,
Like a riptide streaming down a river,
Faces mutate
As your loved ones cry,
You slip through their cold, caring fingers,
You lie helpless,
Feeling the horrible lurching sensation
As your last working muscle is infiltrated,
Bacteria triumphs in their opponents' lifeless flesh.
The cure comes like a white knight through darkness,
Its message is a song of happiness and joy,
A light beaming through infinite blackness,
It fails,
The infected have no hope,
The epidemic wins and wipes out all life.

Edwin Evelyn-Rahr (13)
Langley Park School for Boys

Cultures Poem

There's Chinatown and Oxford Street,
Piccadilly's the place to meet,
Fancy a curry? Try Brick Lane,
You can get there easily by train.

Hatton Garden is the place to find gold,
If you want some, here is where it will be sold,
Temples, mosques and synagogues,
Oh look, that man over there is wearing clogs!

Whoever you are, no matter where you are from,
You could be Leroy, Sarah, Ali or Tom,
We all blend in, we all get along.

So if you're from India, Africa or Spain,
Underneath the colour of your skin,
We're really just the same!

Joe Jefford (12)
Langley Park School for Boys

Anger!

Anger is an emotion that builds up inside you,
You take it out on someone who despises you!
It can be caused by hatred and stress,
You can get angry by even losing a game of chess!
Anger makes you upset and makes you lose control!
You start kicking things around and stub your toe!
Everyone has anger bubbling inside them,
Some people may conceal it, few women and men!
Anger is brought on by many bad emotions,
When you're angry, relax, there isn't a happy potion!
When someone is angry, try to calm them down,
But be pleasant or they will fling you around!
In life, when people agitate you just walk away,
Save the bother they're the ones who will pay!
It helps to stay calm in life, there is a reason!
If you stay calm you will become a respected person!

Harry Birch (13)
Langley Park School for Boys

The First Kiss

Each footstep hitting the floor with gentle ease,
In silence, scared, I wait,
The only sound I can feel is the blood pumping round
                                  my veins,
Time stands quietly still, as I wait listening through
                                 the dense brick wall.

Appearing through the doorway, a face I've learnt to trust
Beaming a smile, that cuts across his face,
Tears rolling from his laughing eyes,
As his arms surround me like a cover warming a child.

Dad leads me from this room,
Down dreary, white, bright, unending corridors,
Then clattering hustle bustle bursts over me,
As swing-doors open, revealing joy.

Baby sister's real, no longer an image in imaginations,
With fingers, toes and nose,
She's there wrapped in love,
Feeling a sense of possession,
Cuddling her, pulling her towards my lips.
They brush her forehead,
She smells so milky sweet,
The first kiss.

George Haylett (12)
Langley Park School for Boys

The War Goes On!

'The war is over,'
Well that's what Blair said.
We celebrated from Scotland to Dover,
And yet so many more are dead.

The Iraqis were thankful,
Full of praise,
But now they're hateful,
No more happy days.

Cheers went around as Saddam was locked up,
People in the streets roared,
It was as if they'd won the cup,
The drinks poured and poured,

A few months on and the soldiers were back,
Iraqis felt under threat,
And soon started an attack,
Blair said, 'We've no regrets!'

So a year and a half on,
And the war still goes on.

Rob Horgan (13)
Langley Park School for Boys

The Miserable Dance

The sky is still dark, you're still asleep,
You trudge miserably on, you could almost weep,
Why is life so unfair? What's the point of it all?
At half seven in the morning, why do we have to go to school?
You're sluggish and cold, your cheeks puffy and red,
And just to think right now, you could be curled up in bed.

Carrying a ton of bricks, packed up to the hilt,
As time goes on, your shoulders start to wilt,
It's so frustrating, we robotically march,
A sea of maroon, the miserable dance!

Dominic Oliver (12)
Langley Park School for Boys

Oscar The Cat

Oscar is a ginger tom,
With the cutest face on Earth,
Although very mischievous,
Only 9 weeks old from birth!

He climbs up our chimney,
But doesn't really care,
One day he's going to get stuck,
Surely that's unfair!

When he's dozing in his bed,
Purring in his dream,
After being fed 3 times a day,
He still wants my whipped cream!

Playing with all his feline toys,
With his sharp and digging claws,
Oh what havoc he has caused,
How much destruction with those little paws!

Joshua Crowhurst (12)
Langley Park School for Boys

Maja Auser

(Maja Auser - it will be fun)

Fox-hunting is fun for everyone,
This is such a lie.
The dogs run, the foxes run,
And they are tortured until they die.

'Get him Spike! Tear him apart!'
The farmer said, as if he had no heart.
And the fox started running as fast as a dart.

The farmer had absolutely no shame,
The farmer doesn't care.
To them it's all a fun game,
As they say, 'Maja Auser.'

Shanil Chande (13)
Langley Park School for Boys

Emotions

Anger, the fiery, red substance
That explodes with rage and fury,
From a little fight, to committing assault,
It builds and grows inside us and lashes out when ready
Anger is a dangerous thing.

Laughter, an uncontrollable emotion
That brings a smile to everyone's face,
Filling us with happiness and joy,
Bubbling and infectious,
Laughter is the best of all.

Sadness, filled with sickness and depression,
We are all sad some time in our lives,
Sadness is the most horrible of all,
Making people lonely,
Or even losing their self-respect.

Jealously, the emotion that can destroy us,
The feeling of want, not need,
The green-eyed monster inside, ripping us apart,
Or it might lead to hatred and loss of friends,
It can cause sadness and anger.
Let's all just laugh!

Stephen Carter (12)
Langley Park School for Boys

Love For What? - Beslan Siege

First day back to school,
We met and talked about our holidays,
Then we were all called into the hall,
There we discovered we were all fools.

Bombs lay all around us,
Waiting to be set off,
The children screamed beside us,
I daren't even cough.

Boom! Boom! Everyone scrambled for the nearest exist,
The fired upon innocent children,
I ran like I've never run before,
It was like a witch's cauldron.

I managed to escape,
Then the soldiers went in,
But my friends left too late,
And got slaughtered in all the hate.

I hate them for what they did,
They said I would be all right, I was only a kid,
And I could recover,
But it was too late.

Ashley Wiles (13)
Langley Park School for Boys

Morals And Ethics

Stiff. The nurse paced to where her patient lay.
A grim habit-forged-smile etched into her brow.
But compassionless, the nurses must stay.
For with a black veil, this hospice is shrouded.

The drugs can only numb the shallower pain.
Not the fear.
'Terminally ill,' the doctors proclaim.
Into the cold unknown the invalids peer.
Their torpid fading is the source of their shame.

But beneath the dejection, is there a glimmer of hope?
Buried by the short-sighted 'Morals and Ethics'.
A trusted hand, a needle of morphine, and under the veil
                                                    they could cope.
But euthanasia is subdued, comfort confined to anaesthetic.
Why do animals have the right to die with dignity?
We are left to suffer until it's too late.
'Let us die with our loved ones,' anarchists plea.
Anger at the restraints of, 'Do not resuscitate.'

The faceless officials, blind to the 18,000 wide bid.
Jailing the makeshift saviours.
But the protesters are masked from the tabloids - well hid.
The government demonising 'killers' for their sacrificial favours.

Ill, with no redemption, no hope anymore.
Is it murder
Or liberation? I'll let you decide.
But trapped out in the cold at death's door.
Would you rather die?

Edward Stone (13)
Langley Park School for Boys

Disaster Strikes

In the lonesome depths of the ice-cold Atlantic, he is seething.
Blissfully unaware, man stands, content, calm.
The waves at sea begin to roar like a baby teething,
The fates of so many lives are in his palms.
As he approaches, the winds strengthen, the tides rise.
A warning is issued, 'Evacuate the area'. Everyone promptly obeys.
Suddenly you feel the wind, the *wind!* Then you realise,
Only the most foolish of fools would ever wish to stay.

'Quickly, he's here. Take cover!' A parade of stumbling and falls.
With a tremendous crash he hits, causing smashed windows
and doors,
Phone lines flattened, making it impossible to make emergency calls,
Roofs of buildings blown clear off, like paper being blown off the floor.
Windows shaking and shattering, doors' hinges buckling and breaking.
There's thunder and lightning as an ominous cloud sits.
To everyone this terror is an awful nightmare in the making,
As the Sunshine State falls to bits.

Suddenly he stops. It's all over. Everything's calm again.
As the traffic builds up from the evacuees' return.
On the sides, trees and signposts are down in their tens.
Every building in sight has crashed and burned.

They say he's the worst they've had in 12 years,
But opinion may vary.
To everyone's eyes that have seen him, he has brought sadness
and tears,
And no one ever again wants to feel the wrath of *Hurricane Charley!*

Tom Williams (13)
Langley Park School for Boys

How Could They?

I was living with my family,
Having a good life,
Having three children,
And my beautiful wife.

One day we had an argument,
And then she left my life,
But then we went to court,
And for my children we fought.

I might have lost the battle,
But I will win the war,
I will see my children weekly,
When I open their bedroom door.

Two years on, I've seen them twice,
I thought I'd try and roll the dice,
I climbed onto a famous place,
The whole world willing to face.

Got myself put in jail,
But the next day I was out on bail,
Saw my kids for one last time,
But then it was like they were not mine.

Stephen Roche (13)
Langley Park School for Boys

Magnolia

My rabbit is called Magnolia,
And I love feeding her.
Hopping,
Sniffing,
She smells all the flowers in the garden.
She also loves eating the cauliflower at the back of the garden.
She likes jumping over my nan's legs and Luis'.
I love her to bits.

Antonia Martinez (11)
Marjorie McClure School

Cars

Going fast
Lots of different colours
Noisy engines
Sports cars zoom along
Many shapes and sizes
Loud music playing
Power steering
Air bag
Rear wash/wipe
Automobile
Vehicle
Estate
Hatchback
Racing cars
Saloon
Taxi
Motor car
Convertible
Coupe
Jeep
Limousine
Tourer.

Ethan Middleton (14)
Marjorie McClure School

Unicorns

Unicorns are magical
Nice and pretty

I think they are fast
Clever and mystical

One horn
Rhino horn

Nervous and twitchy
Shy and silent.

Katie Mott (11)
Marjorie McClure School

Marjorie McClure

M onday morning is an awful time
A rt is my best lesson today - hooray!
R ush to get changed for PE
J umping up and down, the trampoline is fun
O h no it's maths again
R un outside to play football with my friends
I nside again for English
E verybody's working hard

M y hand starts aching
C omputers are next on the list
C lick the mouse and off we go
L earn about anything on the Internet - it's brilliant!
U sed up all my energy now
R eady to go home
E nd of the day - start again tomorrow.

Fozia Sarfraz (14)
Marjorie McClure School

Game Cube

I play on my game cube.
I play on it every day, for hours.
I like it so much.
I play on Super Mario Sunshine.
I play on it for a very long time.
I play on it, on my own, in my bedroom.
I play on it for ages, I like it so, so, so much.
I don't play on the other games anymore,
Super Mario Sunshine is the best game ever.
I love it so much, I feel like I'm on a vacation.
I love it so, so, so, so much.

Christian Bush (14)
Marjorie McClure School

A Poem For My Mum

J is for jokes, Mum always made us laugh.
A is for affectionate, she was a loving person.
C is for cuddles, she was a hugable mum.
K is for kind, she was kind.
I is for intelligent, she was a brainy person.
E is for excellent, she was an excellent darts player.

J is for jolly, she was always happy.
O is for occupying, she was always in order and a
                              hard-working person.
A is for always, always being there for me, Gary and Kerri.
N is for naughty, she was a bit naughty.

S is for sport, she liked tennis and golf.
E is for exciting, she took us to exciting places.
A is for angel, she is watching us.
G is for great, she was the greatest mum in the world.
E is for expert, she was an expert at darts.
R is for real, she was a really good mum.
S is for sweet, she was sweet as well as nice.

Mark Seagers (14)
Marjorie McClure School

The Cat And The Queen

The cat and the queen
Looked after each other.
The queen was called Josie
The cat was called Rosie.

They played a game together
Chasing one another round and round
All the day.

Josie Keeler (13)
Marjorie McClure School

Arsenal Football Club

Every Saturday afternoon
I watch my favourite team
On the television.
I wear my Arsenal shirt of which
I am very proud.
Once I am properly seated
I just shout,
'Arsenal, Arsenal, Arsenal!'
I give them all my support.

Foday Turay (13)
Marjorie McClure School

Rosie

H ides away in her house
A way she goes
M y hamster runs fast
S he sits in her wheel
T eeth bite my finger
E ats her food
R uns about.

Jack Cox (14)
Marjorie McClure School

My Hamster - Kennings

Wheel   spinner
Noise   maker
Dirt   maker
Smell   maker
Wise   teacher
Food   maker
Fun   maker
Fast   runner.

Craig Wilson (11)
Marjorie McClure School

Trips

Trips are all very well

But
I don't like the travelling
I left at 4 in the morning
Happy and excited
Arrived late in the afternoon
Happy and exhausted

But
The trip was enjoyable because
I made some new friends
I met some old friends
It was a great experience

But
The food was absolutely disgusting
And it made me feel sick
Because the quiche tasted horrible
And the mash was all lumpy

But
I thank all the helpers for looking after me
We had a giggle you know.

Nicki Harper (15)
Marjorie McClure School

Web

Tarantula, orange, black
It bites and blows its hairs at you
I shivered as it came out
It moved slowly
It eats flies
It blows sticky gum to stop you
Attacking it.

Kristian Heath (11)
Marjorie McClure School

Just Dancing

I like to tap my feet
When I hear the beat!

I like to dance and move
When I hear the groove!

I like to start to sing
When I hear the ding!

Dancing is really great
You can do it with your mates!

When I feel sad
I put on the music,
I dance and feel glad!

Aphra Kenny-Mastihi (12)
Marjorie McClure School

Dolphins

Fish eaters
Hoop jumpers
Human savers
Sunset watchers
Wave riders
Nosy squeakers

Seabed gliders
Shark beaters
Ball catchers
Seawater glisteners
Group swimmers
Loopy dippers.

Sarah Dowding (11)
Marjorie McClure School

Money

How much money have I got in the bank?
I start with a penny
I start with a pound
I start with a five pound note
I save it
I spend it
I can use it in the shops.
I'll keep it in the bank!
And then I'll add some more again.

Oliver Murray-Brown (13)
Marjorie McClure School

Snooker

Snooker is an exciting game because people like watching
and playing.

I have come very close but I want to win it
because when I did the double on the red
then the crowd clapped . . .
and maybe it is my year
because I would love to win.

Thomas Clements (15)
Marjorie McClure School

Snooker

I like watching it
I like playing it
I like winning

Different coloured balls
Snooker is my game

Everyone shush!

Paul Poulton (15)
Marjorie McClure School

Favourite Things

F avourite thing in the world is my mum.
A ngel is my mum, she is so good.
M y dad is the strongest man in the world.
I ntelligent is my brother, he is so cool.
L azy is my grandad, he sleeps all the time.
Y oghurt is my nan's favourite food.

A dorable are my dogs Sonny and Scrappy.
N oisy is my brother when he doesn't stop talking.
D ata is when I am looking on the computer.

F riendly are my assistants Sue and Frances.
R elationship is something I have with others.
I have a good friend called Mark.
E njoyable is when I am with my family and friends.
N utty is my friend Peter.
D izzy when I don't feel well.
S cared is my friend Lauren I scare her.

Simon Robinson (14)
Marjorie McClure School

When I Look Out Of My Window

When I look out of my window in the morning I see
Grey mist floating through the air.

When I look out of my window I see
Raindrops dripping off the washing line cover.

When I look out of my window I see
Trees blowing this way and that.

When I look out of my window I see
The sky still dark.

Marie Murray (11)
Marjorie McClure School

Riding

I go into the riding school,
When I get on my horse, I feel great.
When I touch my horse, he feels soft
When I listen to my horse, I hear trotting
He will listen to me
My horse makes me jump up in the saddle
My horse nibbles my hair
My horse loves me
My horse's name is Eric
I put my horse in the stable.

Sarah Webb (16)
Marjorie McClure School

Rabbits

Rabbits are soft and cuddly
Always running really fast
Bobbing in and out their cages
Biting the carrots crunch, crunch, crunch
Innocent and vulnerable
Twitching noses
Snoozing and snoozing.

Lauren Hendricks (11)
Marjorie McClure School

Weekends

Swim, swim, swimming away,
Ride, ride, riding today
Play, play, playing
Each day.

Walk, walk, walking the dog
Play, play, playing with the dog
In the park all the day
Passing the time away.

Jordan Findlay (12)
Marjorie McClure School

Dog Kennings

Cat chaser
Mess maker.

Fun, crazy
Very lazy.

Lot big
Some dig.

Lot fuzzy
Called Muzzy.

So fast
Some last.

Chewing bone
Wearing cone.

Very dirty
Very flirty.

Lot hair
Very fair.

Very smelly
Big belly.

Very funny
Chase bunny.

Dirty bowl
Some howl.

Very cute
Furry suit.

Kimberley O'Connor (13)
Marjorie McClure School

If I Were

If I were a dog,
    I would run in the fog.
If I were a cat,
    I would buy a big hat.
If I were a louse,
    I would live in a mouse.
If I were a pig,
    I would wear a wig.
If I were a rat,
    I would lie on the mat.
If I were a hog,
    I would jump on the log.
If I were a moose,
    I would chase a goose.
If I were a bat,
    I would be very fat.
If I were a hen,
    I would write with a pen.

But as I am me,
    I will stay wild and free.

Shane Watson (16)
Parkwood Hall School

Honey And Bunny

I had a dog called Honey
Who had a friend called Bunny.
They went to town to buy two gowns
But they hadn't brought their money.

Then Honey began to moan
Because Honey lost her mobile phone.

'But how have you lost your phone dear Bunny?
You left it at home with your money!'

Amy Maxwell (18)
Parkwood Hall School

Boxing

He became the junior world boxing champion - Lennox
One hot day in Santa Domingo
Olympic gold medal winner South Korea.
Undisputed heavyweight champion of the world.
How many fights I once asked him?
He said, 'Thirty thousand some.'
Thirty-nine wins, two losses.
He has been knocked out twice.
Each time, he came back
And in immediate rematch, knocked his men out.
Mike Tyson was champ in 1992.

Allan Hatton (16)
Parkwood Hall School

Once More With Feeling

I touch the fire
And it freezes me.
I look into it
And it's black.
Why can't I feel my skin?
My skin should crack and peel
I want the fire back.

John Malthouse (16)
Parkwood Hall School

My Team

Charlton Athletic is a football club
All the players are the best a team can have
Charlton have a manager and a coach
Welcome new players to Charlton Athletic.

William Cottrell (17)
Parkwood Hall School

The Boy Who Died Young

When I was one I was always small
When I was two I was not much more
When I was three I was always tall
When I was four I was always cool
When I was five I was always a fool
When I was six I was always at school
When I was seven I acted as if I was eleven
When I was eight I always beat up my mate
When I was nine I learned how to tell the time
When I was ten I made a den
When I was eleven I died and went to Heaven.

Toby Merivale (17)
Parkwood Hall School

Football

I like football
And the biggest clubs give more excitement.
Glory, glory Hunter
Score all the way.
The best team in London
Glory, glory Arsenal.
Last season Arsenal beat every single club
And no team has done it before.
Arsene Wenger got the job done.

Matthew Kong (18)
Parkwood Hall School

Dancing

I go to dancing lessons on Saturdays
We learn a new dance every week.
At 11 o'clock we stop for tea.
I have to get up early every Saturday.

Katie Butcher (18)
Parkwood Hall School

Funny Computers

Computers are always crashing on me
Computers always go wrong
I try to surf the Internet one day at a time
But alas the Internet connection is broken
I do all my school work on the computer
But I can't save my work on the computer
Because there is a virus on it.
Computers are good fun
Because you can go on the Internet
And play games and do homework.
Why don't the computers work for me?

Gareth Flanagan (16)
Parkwood Hall School

Olympic Athlete

There was once an athlete who ran like a greyhound
That always wore himself out,
Was chased by a hound.
His aim was to always come first
So that he would not burst.
He always thought he was the best
So that he could have a test.

David Pithouse (16)
Parkwood Hall School

My Dream

When I was young I used to play football every day
And thought of being a football player
And then when I grew up
I ended up making up a football team
And what a football team it is.

Caroline Allimadi (17)
Parkwood Hall School

My Heart Explodes

Love, a deep emotion
but I am saying it's so deep
and this is your song.
I am saying so emotionally.
And I am telling it from the heart.
It is so pure that I would die
to say that you have got the sweetest eyes
I have ever seen
and I am so deeply in love with you.

Michael Mangan (18)
Parkwood Hall School

Rocky

Rocky is my best film.
I will tell you the names of the people.
Apollo Creed, Rocky, Ivan Drago,
Fluber, Lang II, Tommy Gun.
That's all the boxers
I will tell you the names of the people.
Adrian, Mickey, Uncle Paul.

Joshua Greenslade (16)
Parkwood Hall School

Old Age

When I was 40 I had a job
and when I was 50 I retired from my job,
and when I was 60 I had my pension,
after then I shrunk into 70,
and you know what happened next?
I flew into the sky . . .

Jackie Tuong (16)
Parkwood Hall School

What Does It Matter?

It matters because you are the tempest and I am the cliff,
It matters because every day your rage doesn't hesitate,
It matters because in the same way my strength will not reciprocate.

My demise will only constitute for your rapid reprise,
The bitter aftertaste of my annihilation can only cause
                          assumptions and godly connotation,
I've been branded and stung,
Yours is the only water which can so torridly run,
Through these veins,
Endless pain.

We are an equilibrium of souls,
No matter what our goals,
It matters therefore because of this,
We live in this ambiguous abyss,
Yet in this life and the next,
What are we but comrades living each day as we did the latter,
How can you then ask?
My love, it doesn't matter.

Alfrún Gísladóttir (16)
The Grammar School for Girls, Wilmington

Shadow

There I was standing in the moonlight staring over the hills,
The wind was howling giving me the chills.
There was a shadow, dark, deep and black,
A hand ran down my hunched up back.
I stood there in the silence, the wind rustling my hair,
My heart was thumping but I didn't care.
I carried on walking, the shadow still there,
I couldn't stop now, I was nearly there.
Then finally I reached what I was waiting for,
The shadow was standing in front of the door.
It reached out its hand, it grabbed me before,
This is my story that I tried to tell,
Now here I lay in Heaven and Hell.

Natasha Oliver-Smith (11)
The Grammar School for Girls, Wilmington

The Little Things

Too often we don't realise
What we have until it's gone
Too often we wait too late to say,
'I'm sorry - I was wrong'
Sometimes it seems we don't hold
                    those dearest to our hearts
And allow foolish things
To tear our lives apart.
Far too many times we let unimportant things
                                    into our minds
And then it's usually too late
To see what made us blind
So be sure that you let people know
                    how much they mean to you
Take that time to say the words
Before your time is through.
Be sure that you appreciate everything you've got
And be thankful for the little things
In life that mean a lot.

Laura Carter (15)
The Grammar School for Girls, Wilmington

Friends

Friends are the people who remember your birthday,
They don't take offence from what you say.
They laugh at your worst joke,
They don't tease or provoke!
They are someone to tell your secrets to,
They will always listen to you!
They will never betray your trust!
They will do what they must,
To stay friends with you forever!

Charlotte Lynch (13)
The Grammar School for Girls, Wilmington

Autumn

The season after summer,
Before the winter peak,
Beautiful colours swirling,
Certainly not bleak.

Oranges, yellows, browns,
Leaves swirling to the ground,
Kicked around by wellington boots,
Along to the rustling sound.

The wind blowing through,
Trees shivering in its presence,
Winter desperately trying,
To spread its icy essence.

Autumn begins to show weakness,
In the battle against her foe,
For winter will overpower her,
And she knows she has to go.

She will be back next year,
Trees and leaves and all.
After next summer, before next winter,
Jolly, good old fall.

Kerry Brown (13)
The Grammar School for Girls, Wilmington

I Dream . . .

I dream of calm, quiet and peace,
With naught but birdsong ringing in my ears.
I dream of sitting on the tip of a crescent moon,
Its silvery light reflecting peace and calm
Down to all those slumbering below.
I dream of sailing forth into a sunset,
As it melts away into a velvety midnight sky.
I dream that the love within the heart of a sleeping pup
Could flow through the world
And open the eyes of those blinded by hate.
I dream of standing on a mountain top,
To look out on the crisp, white peaks around me
And understand the true meaning of life.
I dream of lying amongst fallen autumn leaves -
Gold, red and brown - and the bliss I would feel
Just to watch, to listen, to be.
I dream of riding on a chestnut stallion, over blue crystal waters
Towards the voices of angels singing songs of hope.
I dream that all the world would join hands and let the lapping waves
Of a tranquil sea touch their hearts and wash away their fears.
I dream that everyone would stop, be still, for just one moment,
And share this dream with me.

Sarah O'Brien-Wheeler (13)
The Grammar School for Girls, Wilmington

The Water Ripple

Getting changed on the boat, ready to make the splash
A thought whizzing through the mind saying
                    come on, it's waiting for you
You enter, seeing fishes swimming around
Your friends jumping in making ripples in the water
You run and slip off the boat, a huge bow wave
A sound of a belly flop, a very deep sound
Like a cage door slamming shut
You fall and bang your head on the boat
Your friends suddenly screaming in despair
Pulling you up to the surface of the water
Trying, trying harder but too deep
The air pressure and the deepness of the water pulling you down
Like I was on a lead unconscious,
I was struggling to swim up but I couldn't
The current dragging me down and the waves lashing out at me
And taking me down by the great propeller
And the slight bubbles on the surface of the water
Telling that my breath, couldn't hold much longer
I could just hear the slight echo of my friends' voices
Saying, 'Stop the boat's engine, stop the boat's engine!'
And then the propeller stopped gently, twisting, slowly stopping
My friends then grabbing hold of my shirt and pulling me up
Then I gasped for breath as I reached the top
                    and was pulled onto the boat for safety
Now I will carry on my hobby like a fish and see blue again!

Hannah Eastwood (11)
The Grammar School for Girls, Wilmington

Beslan

I used to be happy, I used to be safe
But that's all changed, now that hate has had its way.

On the first of September, the first day of school
I took flowers with me and wore my best clothes.

At School Number One, my friends started screaming.
I ran into school, but terror followed in.

They made us go to the gym, and brought in some corpses.
One of which was my uncle, and I could do nothing but cry.

They said, 'Pray to Allah,' but I prayed to Jesus
I thought of my mum, I had to stay alive for her.

After two awful days, I was shocked awake
By gunshots and explosions. I made a hasty break.

The ceiling caved in, soon there would be nothing.
I jumped through the window, shattering glass on the way.

I ran in one direction, and then to the other.
I bumped into a policeman, and then it was over.

All I remember is waking up is hospital.
My mum hugged me tight, we were both lucky.

There are still people missing, like my cousins.
I am alive, but loved ones are dead.

I pray every day for my cousin's return
But there's little hope and it's fading each day.

But one day I hope to forgive, we must stop this fighting
But now at eleven all I can see is hate.

Claire Martin (11)
The Grammar School for Girls, Wilmington

My Dog

I have a dog,
She is called Maisy.
I love her loads,
She's like a daisy.

I have a dog,
She is my best friend.
I love her loads,
She's like a gem.

I have a dog,
She is the best.
I love her loads,
She's not a pest.

I have a dog,
She is my guard.
I love her loads,
She's *very* hard.

I had a dog,
She was the best of best.
I loved her loads,
She's been put to rest.

Lucy Billing (11)
The Grammar School for Girls, Wilmington

Autumn

Autumn is here,
It's really boring.
Everyone's indoors,
Almost snoring.

Black skies ahead,
Here comes the rain.
Lots of big puddles,
Around the drain.

Slushy leaves,
All around.
Making it dirty,
On the ground.

Walking to school,
In the thundery rain.
Here it comes,
Once again.

Hallowe'en is
Nearly here.
Yes, it's that
Time of year.

Autumn has been,
Autumn has gone.
Next is winter,
Yeah! Much more fun.

Sophie Rawlinson (11)
The Grammar School for Girls, Wilmington

Winter

Winter is almost here,
The hedgehogs have gone to bed,
Lying in their bundle of leaves,
People might think they're dead,
The snow is falling to the ground,
Like the floor of clouds in Heaven,
The badgers sit in their sets,
With children six or seven,
But humans indoors all tucked up and cosy,
Waiting for the time of year
When Santa comes at night,
The trees sit in the cold,
Their branches torn and battered,
While the squirrels sit inside them,
All bored and fatted,
They think it's time to sleep
And have a pleasant winter,
So when you're at home think of them
And may your dreams be merry.

Emma O'Brien-Wheeler (12)
The Grammar School for Girls, Wilmington

Winter

Penguins live in igloos,
With snowmen built outside.
Eskimos wear hats and scarves
And stand along beside.

Frost clouding up the windows,
Icicles hanging down.
Snow is really falling,
So I will not frown.

I like it when it snows,
Snow is really cool.
I especially like it in the winter,
So I can get off school.

Joanna Moore (12)
The Grammar School for Girls, Wilmington

The Glamorous Ship

The glamorous ship
went sailing by.
The sails so big,
the mast so high.

A storm came brewing,
the crew were ruined.
The poor, lost captain at sea.

The waves came over,
the fish too.
I wouldn't go sailing
near the Isle of Caboo.

So make up your mind
about sailing with me,
but if I were you,
I'd go to sea.

Megan Heath (13)
The Grammar School for Girls, Wilmington

Cocker Spaniels

This is the dog that is the best,
So much better than all the rest.
They are playful and friendly,
Its fur so soft and cuddly.
It needs quite a lot of care,
But the cost is quite fair.
I don't think spaniels are too big,
I don't think that they are a biting type of dog.
They play with either people or toys,
I don't think they make too much noise.
They are a gun dog,
They can hunt all night,
Not to be scared of fright,
But this can only happen if you treat them right.
Treat dogs with care!

Rebecca Williams (11)
The Grammar School for Girls, Wilmington

Moving On

A mountain of sadness fills me as I stare into my best friend's eyes,
A river of tears fall down my cheeks, as I say my last goodbyes.
Oh what, oh what can I say that will make this feeling go away,
I look around at all the faces I'll be leaving behind today.
I say to myself, don't cry, it's just a school.

However, no matter how hard I try,
I cry and cry the rivers of tears,
For it's not just a school,
There's my friends and memories here.

Again a mountain of sadness fills
As I cry my last goodbyes.
I try a weak smile,
But fresh tears leak out instead.

So we leave and go our separate ways,
But I still have that feeling inside me,
I can't push that away,
But now, oh wow I can finally see the sun.

Bethany Hobbs (11)
The Grammar School for Girls, Wilmington

Seasons

First comes spring, with all the flowers and trees,
The singing of the birds, and the buzzing of the bees.

Next is summer, bringing all the heat,
The time for eating cold ice cream and wearing nothing on your feet.

Autumn follows summer, when all the trees are tall,
But they're not very pretty when their leaves begin to fall.

Last comes winter, the time when snowflakes fall,
But winter wouldn't be winter without snowflakes and snowballs!

Summer, winter, autumn, spring, the divisions of the year,
Enjoy them while they last as the next one's very near!

Natasha Dillon (12)
The Grammar School for Girls, Wilmington

The Knightly Gnome

In red-hot summer sun,
giggly fairies having fun.

Amongst the grass, no one dare roam,
creeps a careless, but brave knightly gnome.

Fairies gasp at the sight,
a dashing, daring, noble knight.

The smell of sunflowers fills the air,
leprechauns dance without a care.

With his suit of steel,
to the fairies he looks unreal.

Steadily, he marches on his crusade,
remembering all the mistakes he'd made.

Tripping over here and there,
the clumsy knight falls everywhere.

At last he finds his way out,
suddenly he hears a shout.

It was the fabulous fairy king,
with his daughter and a ring.

'Will you take my daughter's hand?
The wedding will be awfully grand!'

The knight said, 'Yes,' quite happily,
the king and daughter smiled with glee.

At last the knight had finished his quest,
now safe at home with his fairy princess.

Paige Smith (11)
The Grammar School for Girls, Wilmington

The Mysterious World

I sit amongst the flowers,
The shafts of light coming through the gaps of the trees.
The legs of the trees crawling everywhere on the ground.
The warm sunlight on my face.
The flowers cushioning me below.
The tall trees looming over me,
Their twiggy fingers scratching at my skin.
This is the mysterious forest.

I walk round and round these trees,
Winding and winding,
Choosing a different path each time.
The flowers and grass in-between my toes,
They are soft to the touch.
There are trees everywhere.
Leaves have fallen from the trees
And the flowers have started dying.

The royal blue sky above,
The fluffy white clouds.
The dark, black nights,
With their twinkling lights.
The flocks of birds,
With their silky, feathery skin,
That moves in the breeze, to and fro.
This is the mysterious sky.

I could fly forever in the open sky,
But it is getting colder and colder.
The flowers are gone,
The trees are bare.
There are more clouds than sky.
The navy blue clouds roam the world above,
Taking up every inch of space,
The twinkling lights can no more be seen.

Nicola Kinnear (12)
The Grammar School for Girls, Wilmington

Death

Death is creeping up from behind.
There's the road of death,
There's death,
There's the house of death.
Death is everywhere,
Beware.

Death is in Iraq,
Death is in Europe,
Death is in America.
Death is everywhere,
Beware.

Death is in the room,
Death is in your house,
Death is in hospitals,
Death is out and about.
Death is everywhere,
Beware.

Beware not to be caught,
As death is creeping around,
Following you everywhere is death,
Be careful wherever you are
As death is everywhere,
Beware!

Charlotte Spitter (13)
The Grammar School for Girls, Wilmington

Last Christmas

Christmas Eve has finally come
One more day to go
We're all going to the panto
Hale and Pace, top the show

Dick Whittington was the panto's name
It really was good fun
Then we went to Andy's house
And Christmas Eve was done

How tight we closed our eyes that night
To make our dreams come true
It surely would be a plight
If Santa bumped into you

No snow did come on Christmas Day
That really was a shame
How boring when the sun did shine
It's really not the same

All my presents, were what I'd hoped
I screamed and cheered out loud
I don't know how Santa coped
But he really did us proud

Christmas dinner was superb
Crackers we did pull
I shared one with my daddy
And the present hit the wall

I'd like to end my poem
With this message to you
Christmas Day was really fun
I hoped you enjoyed it too!

Sophie Butler (11)
The Grammar School for Girls, Wilmington

Thirteen

Year 9 and times are changing fast,
My childhood years are in the past,
Teenage years ahead of me,
After this, university?

Outside of school it's pretty near,
Something to help me with my career,
I joined a thing called the ATC,
Taking opportunities that come to me.

Lectures studying and lots of fun,
And now I'm not the only one,
Who has exams we want to pass
And get our blues pretty fast.

But at this time in the present,
Some things are not very pleasant,
Terrorism I don't find fair,
The things included tend to scare.

Many things never change I see,
Third world starvation still to me,
A problem that they always keep trying,
To give them food and stop them dying.

So the world is changing day to day,
Not for the better I hear people say,
This is my life as it seems,
And I have just turned thirteen.

Lara Escane (13)
The Grammar School for Girls, Wilmington

Girls Are So Much Better Than Boys!

Girls are better than boys
'Cause they don't mess around with their baby toys
We have beautiful long hair
And we know it's what boys can't bear
We always try our best
And we never stop for a rest!
We always keep clean
Boys are so mean!
We always keep fit
And never forget our PE kit!
We love going to the shops
Looking for new tops!
We love wearing rings
But then again boys love a bit of bling!
Just admit it, girls are so much better than boys!

Hannah Chummun (12)
The Grammar School for Girls, Wilmington

Who Is She?

Her long black hair covered her eyes,
She's there!
She bangs on the floor
And scratches the doors.
She's there!
She looks through the window,
You can't see her, though
She's there!
Where did she come from?
Nobody knows!
She has a habit of screaming with fright
All through the night.
She's there!
I say,
'She's there!'

Alice Fortune (11)
The Grammar School for Girls, Wilmington

Guardian Angel

Your bright blue, burning eyes never stray from me,
Your lithe figure, draped in white silk moves swiftly to my aid,
Your delicate fingers hold the hands of time,
And keep them in my favour.

You guide me when the path is unclear,
And steer me onto the right track when I stray onto the bad,
Your footsteps always lead me,
And when I can walk no more you carry me.

You stop mirrors cracking and gather the salt when it is spilt,
Your soft, downy wings rustle in the gentlest of breezes,
And when I forget how to fly, you lift me.

Your tousled, dark waves of hair frame your handsome face,
Your body always warms me when the north wind bites,
You are always by my side, my guardian angel.

Hannah Walker (13)
The Grammar School for Girls, Wilmington

Cold Winter Nights

The thing that I love about cold winter nights
Is being at home, warm, as snug as a bug
When the wind blows it rattles the windows with a sharp snap
But I'm safe inside with hot chocolate in my favourite mug.

The thing that I love about cold winter nights
Is eating crumpets hot from the toaster
Which warm me through from nose to toe
I sit and dream of hot, sunny days and seeds to sow in spring.

The thing that I hate about cold winter nights
Is the fingers of darkness stealing away the day
Feet twisted and tied in thick, woolly tights
The silence of the outside birdsong gone,
Playful voices, ghosts of summer.

Bethany Hedges (13)
The Grammar School for Girls, Wilmington

Do You Promise?

Do you promise there will be no more wars,
no more, no more, no more?
Do you promise our country will be safe,
for the whole human race?
Do you promise our children shall not be harmed,
this means no one should be armed?
Do you promise we will be free,
I mean everyone not just me?
Do you promise to treat everyone the same,
that can always be our aim?
Do you promise you will get along,
just like in a beautiful song?
Do you promise we will have peace,
this means fighting should cease?
Do you promise you will trust,
that's a must?
Do you promise families won't be torn,
so babies can be born?
If you believe in me,
we can change the world - you'll see.

Stephanie Johnson (12)
The Grammar School for Girls, Wilmington

Why Elephants Can't Fly

Have you ever wondered,
Why elephants can't fly.
Do you have an answer,
Oh please tell me why.

Maybe their feet are just too large,
Or they're as heavy as a very large barge.
I don't think it'll be their feet,
They're just too big for the airline seat.

Abby Fewtrell (12)
The Grammar School for Girls, Wilmington

Miss, Miss

Miss, Miss, I have got a nose bleed
Miss, Miss, I have got the flu
Miss, Miss, I have broken my arm
Miss, Miss, I feel sick!

Miss, Miss, I think I'm dead
Miss, Miss, I have pen on my face
Miss, Miss, I need to get my coat
Miss, Miss, I have to see the head teacher!

Miss, Miss, I need a drink
Miss, Miss, I have to collect my bag
Miss, Miss, I need to get my PE kit
Miss, Miss, I am going to faint!

Miss, Miss, I have got double vision
Miss, Miss, I need my medication
Miss, Miss, I left my jumper in the hall
So . . . please can I go to the toilet!
(Because I'm too embarrassed to ask!)

Mica Clements (11)
The Grammar School for Girls, Wilmington

The Bluebird

The lake blue, below the hill.
Over it, as I looked, there flew
Across the waters, cold and still,
A bird whose wings were palest blue.

The sky above was blue at last
The sky beneath me blue in blue
A moment as the bird, it passed
Caught his image as he flew.

Amber Macintosh (14)
The Grammar School for Girls, Wilmington

Darkness

In the darkness I lay
In my soft, white, fluffy sheets
There is silence
Darkness all around me
Until the street lamp flickers on
I try to close my eyes
Bang!
A door slammed hard
The noise has turned to silence again
I can still hear the echo in my head
It disappears
I try to remember
I think hard
I give up
But before I have a chance . . .
Too late
My eyes are closing
My head feels heavy
Drifting into a deep sleep
Darkness all around.

Georgina Purcell (11)
The Grammar School for Girls, Wilmington

I Dream Of A World

I dream of a world
Where everyone is sweet,
A place full of niceness
Where you like who you meet.

I dream of an earth,
Where there are no drugs,
Gambling or boozing
Terrorists or thugs.

I dream of a globe
Where peace is present,
Where there are no bullies
And everything is pleasant.

I want to be able to live this dream
Be part of that magical place,
Be proud to stand up and say
I'm part of the human race.

And when that day is finally here
I think the whole world will stand up and cheer.

Kelly Stevenson (12)
The Grammar School for Girls, Wilmington

Who Needs Words?

Who needs words,
When we speak from the heart?
Who needs words,
When we have expressive art?

Who needs words,
When you know what I'm thinking?
Who needs words,
When they just end up sinking?

Who needs words,
When actions speak for themselves?
Who needs words,
When we could dig deeper and delve?

So who needs words so much that it hurts?
Who can't live without any of these things?
   . . . I can't . . .
Because words are what make me soar through the air,
They are my bold, widespread, powerful wings.

Nadia Narayan (12)
The Grammar School for Girls, Wilmington

Freedom

Freedom is special.
Free is something everyone should be.
Free is not to be locked away and throwing away the key.
Free is running through the wind, hair blowing in your face.
Free is being able to break away.
Freedom is a feeling from inside,
Deep, deep down in your heart.

Emily Allen (13)
The Grammar School for Girls, Wilmington

Will You?

'Will you be my valentine?
Will you marry me, oh June?
Will you lock me in the basement
On a full moon?

Will you bring me millions of roses?
Will you bring chocolate sweets
Once a month until I stop?
Will you feed me lots of treats?

Will you treat me with lots of devotion?
Will you say bless you, when I sneeze?
Will you dust my back with powder
Just in case I've got the fleas?

Will you be my angel?
Will you be my dream?'
That's exactly what the horseman
Said to Lady Cream.

Demi Adenekan (11)
The Grammar School for Girls, Wilmington

The Jaguar

This fearless animal is as black as night,
If you are wise you will not fight.
How many times has he fed
And how many times have humans bled?
His eyes gleam brightly like a star,
As all will know who bear the scar,
Of the fiercest of the jungle beasts,
Beware, you might become one of his feasts.
He knows when you are near or far,
Yes, he is the jaguar.

Lauren Pickard (11)
Weald of Kent Grammar School for Girls

The Rainforest

R ain planting itself on my frail body
A nxious, I hear the disturbing noise of the toucans
I nsects talk in-between the rushing river
N ervous I twist through the long draping vines
F ungi of all shapes creep around the undergrowth
O ver the sneaky snake, I step towards the sly jaguar
R eally paralysed, I think of all the animals that are camouflaged.
    I can't see
E vil tapirs eating near the river
S loths hang from the canopy watching cautiously
T he rainforest!

Emma Gilham (11)
Weald of Kent Grammar School for Girls

My War Poem

Planes were flying overhead.
I looked to the left they were all dead!
Then to the right not much better.
I went over to my dead friend I took out a letter
I read, it was to his wife
I opened it with a knife
A fan of bullets sped overhead!
I jumped up and felt the lead.
I had been shot in the arm!
I wished I was back on the farm.

I crawled towards a tank.
It looked like it was flanked.
It was by two big cars with guns.
I pulled out my gun and shot the tank, it exploded.
I had killed many men, I was obviously spotted.
A small dot appeared on my jacket a red dot?
Bang, the red dot was replaced by a bullet wound.
I was dead.

Glen Watts (12)
Wilmington Grammar School for Boys

My Baby Tiger

My baby tiger is small and cute,
He always makes me laugh when he is playing with me,
He likes to watch TB because of the bright colours he sees,
When he is angry, he shows his sharp claws to tell people no one
should go near him,
I am glad of my baby tiger.

My baby tiger is soft and sweet,
He jumps with joy when he sees food at first sight,
When he is sad he sprints up to my room and tucks into my duvet,
He is happy when I treat him,
I am glad of my baby tiger.

My baby tiger has grown now,
He has grown sharp teeth so he can chew meat,
He keeps on roaring every day and night and I don't get any sleep,
When he is angry, he threatens people, by showing his sharp teeth,
I am glad of my pet tiger.

My grown tiger is king of the kingdom,
He likes to control the house,
He is getting too old staying in this house and there is nowhere for
him to stay.
I rang up the zoo to tell them that my pet tiger can no longer stay
because he was taking up too much room,
I am sad that my pet tiger is going.

My grown tiger is leaving my house now, I am feeling down,
It is going to be quiet without him and all alone,
I will have a good night's sleep when he is gone,
There will be no more fun without my pet,
I feel like crying but I can't.

It is the day my pet is going, it is very sad,
I am trying to remember the times we had fun together,
The zookeepers are here now to take my pet away,
I can't sleep because of what I have done,
I am all alone because my pet tiger is not here.

Fahim Khan (11)
Wilmington Grammar School for Boys

Homework

Homework time has come again
It feels like I'm on an endless train
One homework finished another starts
Maths, English, history, art
So many subjects I'm getting confused
Oh no almost all of my time has been used
Also technology, geography too
The deadline's tomorrow what can I do
I do not need any bad attention
I do not want a detention
Mountains of books, rivers of ink
They fill up my brain until I can't think
Finally now everything's done
Drat I've missed out a sum
So many books my shoulders sag
I cannot carry this heavy bag!

Jamie Walker (11)
Wilmington Grammar School for Boys

It Was A Rainy Day

The rain was pouring down,
So I was glum and had a frown,
I got on the bus,
Made no fuss,
When I got to school,
I felt such a fool.

I had forgotten my homework,
And my English teacher was such a berk,
I was gonna be in so much trouble,
I really needed a big cuddle,
But wait a minute, no need to worry,
The teacher was absent from the effects of a dodgy curry.

Jonathan Sutcliffe (12)
Wilmington Grammar School for Boys

Fog

The wrath-like mist and swirling fog
Were duly noted in the liner's log.
The captain ordered a sharp lookout
For fear of other ships about,
For these were the days long gone by
Before the time of the electronic eye
When the only aid a captain was given,
Was a pair of eyes and a prayer to Heaven.

And then came that dreaded shout
'Iceberg ahead, look out, look out.'
Alas the warning was not in time,
The liner was new and in her prime
Her speed was such it couldn't be checked,
She was doomed that moment to be holed and wrecked
She lay dead in the water, her boats all around,
As slowly she dipped to her resting ground,
The graveyard fathoms below,
Where all ships have to go.
Her once bright lights and lofty might would
For evermore out of sight

And when they asked the reason why
The once proud ship came to die,
They found the answer in the captain's log.
I lost my ship because of fog.

David Wenzel (12)
Wilmington Grammar School for Boys

PlayStation Games

Driver 3 is fast and quick,
Mafia scenes can make you sick,
Tony Hawks is oh so cool,
Red Dead Revolver is nobody's fool,
Star Wars game has planets and sun,
The Simpsons game is out and fun.

Joe Perry (11)
Wilmington Grammar School for Boys

Autumn

The leaves are falling heavily
Along the cobbled road,
The weather is all cold and sad,
And the trees are all but bare.

The nights are getting darker,
There is a lot more rain,
All the children sleeping,
They can't go out to play.

There are no animals about,
Hibernating in their nests,
Warming up their newborn babies,
They will be out next year.

And while Christmas is returning,
And spring is on its way,
Just think of all the good old things
That you could do next year.

Andrew Norman (14)
Wilmington Grammar School for Boys

Inside My Head

I see the beauty of the sea
Ships go by crumbling the water.
The sun illuminating each crease of the sales
The shadow causing my vision to falter.

I see three vibrant doors glaring into my eyes
Each door representing a room of surprise.
Which door shall I enter, it's up to me
Number one, two or three.

I see an invitation of chips swarming the plate
Piles of hot, greasy, steam that I cannot wait.
Fat ones, curly ones, chunky or small
Which ones shall I choose, or shall I take them all.

Sam Ward-Corderoy (12)
Wilmington Grammar School for Boys

Elephant Began

Elephant began,
He took some brushy bristles,
He took a slender rope,
For his tail.

For his ears,
He stole angel wings,
He stole a leather coat.

From a hunt,
He grabbed a horse's neigh,
He grabbed the sound of a blasting trumpet,
For his voice.

In the dead of night,
He took two brown cocoa beans,
He took the sight of a fiery eagle,
For his beady eyes.

From a deep, dark wood,
He snatched a palm tree's branch,
He snatched a pair of binoculars,
For his trunk

And elephant was made.

Conor Keappock (11)
Wilmington Grammar School for Boys

Animals

Some animals can jump, some animals can fly,
Some can walk, some can say, 'Bye.'
Some animals swim, some animals can slither,
Some can run and some can shiver.
Some are fast, some are slow,
How many animals do you know?
If your animal does other things, just give us a beep,
Remember all animals have to sleep.

Nathan Sundin (11)
Wilmington Grammar School for Boys

What Is It?

While walking through the jungle on a clear summer's day
I saw a creature of strange design chewing on some hay.

I've never seen one like it on any trip I've had
But looking this one in the eye, I thought that I was mad.

It wasn't that it was ugly, or only had three toes
Its colour was quite natural and it had a normal nose.

It didn't have a trunk or antlers big and wide
It didn't have webbed feet or wings stuck on its side.

It didn't have an eye stuck in the middle of its head
Or use a trick which some can do - pretending it was dead.

The thing that made it different from others all around
Is not the way it sang because it didn't make a sound.

It's simply that its head was stuck atop a neck *sooo* long
And until you get more used to it, it really looks quite wrong.

It's the best of all the animals, although it makes you laugh
It's an animal that is quite unique, the tall and proud giraffe.

Daniel Wanostrocht (11)
Wilmington Grammar School for Boys

The Tarty Cow

There was a tarty cow on a dairy farm,
She had a pink udder and she wore lots of lip balm.
She had purple skin and had a diamond bell,
And the perfume she had on was a pongy smell,
She left the stable to meet a bull,
She came home crying, what a fool,
The bull wasn't there to her surprise,
But she met a cat who sucked her milk dry.

Tom Knapp (11)
Wilmington Grammar School for Boys

What Is Life?

Do we have to work and play?
Will it get us through the day?
Every day a child is born,
Every morn there is a dawn.

Do we have to work and play?
Will it get us through the day?
In the day there is bright light,
But this goes out at night.

Do we have to work and play?
Will it get us through the day?
Tell me it is not true,
That the world is turning new.

Do we have to work and play?
Will it get us through the day?
The answer is probably no,
Maybe the world is at a low!

James Nicholls (12)
Wilmington Grammar School for Boys

Sports Heroes Of The World

Mohammed Ali can sting like a bee,
He can take a man, mutant or machine
Zinadine Zidane is very, very skilled,
And when it comes down to it, people get thrilled,
Darren Campbell runs with pride
As he beats the American side.
Tiger Woods can hit a ball far,
He always seems to score on par.
Andy Roddick can smash a ball with pace,
The crowd go wild when he scores an ace.
All our sports heroes have their fame,
They believe in no pain, no gain.

Joe Watt (12)
Wilmington Grammar School for Boys

The Football

The air was cold and damp and Dad and I risked getting a *clamp*.
We parked on the double yellow,
Dad and I thought it was fine.
We went through the turnstiles,
The walk to our seats felt like *miles.*
The match kicked off.

The ball's with Cole, Lampard, *Rooney!*
What a volley, it made me drop my lolly.
The half-time went, up came a cheer,
The man behind me spilt his beer.
The second half started with a bang!

Beckham, Owen, *goal!*
2-0, 'We are the champions,' we sang around the ground
I fell on the floor and found a pound
I went to the shops and spent it.
When I was there, I heard it, the cheer went up, I missed a goal!
I ran up and my Dad said,
'Terry scored with his head.'
The final whistle, we won! We won!
Then I thought of my mum
She must be sad she didn't see the making of history
We went to the shops and bought a lamp
We got to the car and found a clamp!

Jonathan Tedman (11)
Wilmington Grammar School for Boys

I Am A River

I am a river, I hiss like a snake and move slowly and steadily
                                                    like a tortoise.
I glitter like a diamond and sometimes rage like an outrageous dragon.
Then I start to move steadily back to my home.
On the way to my home, I collide with some rocks.
When I am right at the end of the mountain,
I cascade swiftly down the mountain and reach my destiny.

Prasun Kaushik (11)
Wilmington Grammar School for Boys

The Monster

I dreamt a dream about a monster that night,
I woke up with a huge fight,
The monster that had tried to swallow me whole,
Looked like a dragon with a face like a mole,
It had shining great teeth, oh what a sight,
The monster's eyes shone through the night,
With the revolting smell that came from his mouth,
Was in fact children he had eaten down south,
He had slimy green scales,
That slipped and slid from house to house,
Not making a sound but all you could hear was a squeak
from a mouse,

But when I woke up what did I see?
Those great big eyes glaring at me,
It was there in a blink of an eye,
I shivered in fear and whispered, 'Oh my!'
There it waits at the end of my bed,
Snarling and growling . . . nothing more to be said!

Alex Fowler (12)
Wilmington Grammar School for Boys

The Archer

The archer looked forth on the enemy,
Stepped his foot over the line,
Looked forth again,
His left hand rose, with a bow in his hand,
He drew the arrow from the quiver,
He put the arrow on the string,
His head towards the target, he pulled the bow back and back,
Then he let go and his arrow sang,
As it just hit the target of such speed, such grace,
On the bullseye, what a shot!

Rhys Jones (13)
Wilmington Grammar School for Boys

Bad People

Bad men, bad men
What you going to do
What you going to do
When we come for you.

Bad cop, bad cop
What you going to do
What you going to do
When we arrest you.

Bad boys, bad boys
What you going to do
What you going to do
When we shout at you.

Bad teachers, bad teachers
What you going to do
What you going to do
When we punish you.

Lawrence Williams (12)
Wilmington Grammar School for Boys

The Devil Of A Sister!

I have a younger one,
She is not really fun,
I hate her guts, lots of cuts
From her are on my arm.

We sit down to watch some telly,
She hits me on the belly,
I start to cry, Mum says, 'Oh my,'
Dad is pleading for some jelly.

I say, 'That's it, you little creep,
I don't fall for an act that's cheap.
I hate you, you smell like poo!'
And then she starts to weep!

James White (13)
Wilmington Grammar School for Boys

The Boasting Nut

I'm a nut, I'm tasty and big,
I'm a nut and not a dirty pig.
I'm a nut, I'm saltier than the rest,
I'm a nut, I'm simply the best.
I'm a nut, I'm better than you,
I'm a nut, I'm scrumptious to chew.
I'm a nut, I'm top of the pack,
I'm a nut, I make a lovely pub snack.
I'm a nut, I taste good with beer,
I'm a nut, so give me a cheer!
I'm a nut, I love me, me, me,
I'm a nut and not a pea.
Oh no, don't eat me, you ugly man,
You're not like me, top of the clan.
Oh phew, you didn't you stupid nutter,
You put me instead in peanut butter!

Alexander Khawam (12)
Wilmington Grammar School for Boys

Faith

Killing people day by day
Is the job I do every day
I kill with different swords
And I kill with different guns
Who could I be?
I don't know myself
All I know is that my heart is pure
But my character is not
What can I do except kill?
If I have faith I could do anything
I have looked at the bad side of a true person
Let me look at the other
How can I live with love, peace and happiness
I can do it if I have faith.

Saravanan Eswaravel (12)
Wilmington Grammar School for Boys

Football

G is for goal, the ball hitting the back of the net,
R is for referee who will control the game,
E is for England, will we win the World Cup again?
A is for Arsenal, the team I support,
T is for trophy, every team is aiming to win these.

F is for free kick, will they shoot around the wall,
O is for oranges, a half-time snack,
O is for offside, don't get caught doing this,
T is for team, eleven men all together,
B is for ball, you can't play without one,
A is for alcohol, you can't have this while you're playing,
L is for league, separating the best from the worst,
L is for lazy, you can't be this.

M is for magazines, telling you all the latest news,
A is for awful, the feeling when you lose,
T is for transfer, moving to a different team,
C is for cabinet, to hold all your trophies,
H is for hammering, beating a team by lots of goals.

Adam Sams (12)
Wilmington Grammar School for Boys

Xbox And Halo

X box rules,
B ig it is,
O nly good games,
X box really does rule.

A ll music can go on it,
N ew games all the time,
D umb PS2 is stupid.

H alo rules,
A nd system links 16 players on Halo.
L ose your PS2,
O n the Xbox is where it's at.

Benjamin Urch (11)
Wilmington Grammar School for Boys

Autumn

A ll of the leaves fall in yellows, reds, browns and greens,
U nfortunately it gets colder, to feel warmer, I wear coats and jeans.
T here is the smell of burning from fireworks and giant bonfires.
U nlike the summer, the nights are longer and darker,
M any like October because of Hallowe'en and pumpkins,
N ow is the time to trick or treat and dress like munchkins.

T he ground is wet and hard to ride on,
I get bored with the wet weather and hope for snow soon,
M y friends like throwing and kicking the leaves at each other,
E veryone wants the heating on to stay warm.

Tim Scott (13)
Wilmington Grammar School for Boys

Football

F ast and exciting,
O h no! The defender scored an own goal,
O ranges at half-time,
T ackles come flying in,
B alls being kicked everywhere,
A brilliant run down the wing and a
L ovely finish from the striker,
L oud celebrations all around the stadium.

Joe Olenka (12)
Wilmington Grammar School for Boys

Summer

S is for no snow.
U is for no umbrellas.
M is for no moaning.
M is for no meaning.
E is for no Easter.
R is for no rain.

Aron Thevathasan (11)
Wilmington Grammar School for Boys

Rap Music

R hyming slang,
A microphone in your hand,
P eople on their own rapping, or maybe a band.

M usic is heaven for me,
U p the top of the charts,
S inging is not as strong as rap,
I t touches millions of people's hearts,
C arry on rapping for ever.

Daniel D'Rosario (11)
Wilmington Grammar School for Boys

Autumn

A is for *autumn,* one of the four seasons,
U is for umbrella, might need to be used during this period,
T is for time when the clocks move back,
U is for unhappy when I see rain pouring down outside,
M is for months that slowly pass by,
N is for nevertheless spring will come soon.

Adam Read (13)
Wilmington Grammar School for Boys

My Cats

M is for majestic in the morning,
Y is for youthful as they play.

C is for cuddles when you're sad,
A is for athletic when they smell food,
T is for touching their very soft fur,
S is for sleeping the day away.

Jonathan Nichols (11)
Wilmington Grammar School for Boys

Me!

B ubbly and brilliant
E nergetic and exciting
N ice and neat

L ovely and lazy
O utgoing and obedient
C onfident and capable
K ind and knowledgeable
E xtravagant and enjoyable
T rustworthy and tolerant
T eam member and thoughtful.

Ben Lockett (11)
Wilmington Grammar School for Boys

Macbeth

M ad Macbeth killing all those people,
A nd his psycho wife.
C areful he is trying not to be caught.
B anquo, his best friend still gets killed,
E ver the thought in his mind of killing the king,
T rying to be king,
H orrible is Macbeth, such a weird man.

James Pask (11)
Wilmington Grammar School for Boys

Movies

M ovies are my life, I can't resist a good film,
O n a birthday, a wedding or birth, it's the very best thing on
the Earth.

V ery hard without movies,
I would just howl and howl,
E very day I watch movies and every day I
S hall.

Ben Warner (11)
Wilmington Grammar School for Boys

Rugby

Gumshield in,
Boots on,
I've been waiting so long
For this game,
A chance of minor fame.
That feeling of elation
And sense of congratulation
In the air,
Everywhere.

The game begins the big match,
Yes! I make the first catch
And pass the ball.

Charging down the pitch
In a staggered line.
This chance is mine!
I see the ball and make the call,
'Here pass! Over here!'
The time is near.

I've got space,
I start to quicken my pace,
Yelling as I go.
I get the ball and dive,
Dive for the try line . . .
And score!

David Richards (11)
Wilmington Grammar School for Boys

Limerick

There once was a man from Crewe
He didn't know what to do
He had one leg
The size of a peg
And he couldn't get that size shoe.

Daniel Jeffery (12)
Wilmington Grammar School for Boys

My Friend

My best friend,
Was one in a million.
He got ten out of ten every day,
My best friend was simply the best,
We thought our friendship would never end,
Until the day,
That fateful day,
It seemed like our string of friendship had been cut,
The day he moved was stormy,
I walked through the rain,
To the house next door,
For the last time,
To give him a fond farewell,
Now I have a picture of him,
Which watches me wherever I go,
I will never forget him.

Carl Foster (12)
Wilmington Grammar School for Boys

Death

Death is dark,
It leaves its mark.
Death causes pain,
It turns people insane.
Death is a black fog,
It takes child and dog.
Death is a bad thought,
It strikes in air, town or port.
Death is painful like a black murky pool.

Nicholas Larkins (12)
Wilmington Grammar School for Boys

A Poem About Happiness And Sadness

Happiness is the colour orange,
Happiness tastes like a bar of delicious dark chocolate,
Happiness looks like two people playing joyfully,
Happiness sounds like a bird chirping loudly,
Happiness is like the sun shining down on you forever,
Happiness is like an evening sky,
Happiness feels like snuggling in a warm bed.
So whenever you think about happiness, remember you can taste,
See hear and feel happiness when it is around.

Sadness is the colour grey,
Sadness is like a wilting flower,
Sadness tastes like the poison from a snake's fang,
Sadness looks like a child sitting alone in a playground full of children,
Sadness sounds like a blood-curdling howl,
Sadness is like a dying person's cry for help.
So when you see someone sad, try and comfort them
And get them feeling happy.

Daniel Warling (12)
Wilmington Grammar School for Boys

Autumn

All the colours of the leaves floating down,
gold, red, brown, the leaves that fall,
cover the damp ground below.

Summer is over and winter is almost here,
the warmth has gone,
the cold is here.

A blanket of darkness draws in over the day,
making days smaller,
and nights longer.

The trees stand naked amongst the rows of houses,
but the proud evergreens remain
covered with leaves.

Thomas Greening (13)
Wilmington Grammar School for Boys

Young Writers - Great Minds From Western Kent

Family

I know that we sometimes argue and fuss,
But I know that I love them so much,
They're the light of my fire,
The singing in my heart,
But one thing's for sure, they're *family!*

They are in my heart every day,
And when I get home I shout hooray,
I have a nutty uncle, who lives down the road,
With his wife and his son and daughter, we visit them loads.
But one thing's for sure, they're *family!*

Whatever they do,
Wherever they go,
I'll love them to bits, I hope that they know.

But one thing's for sure, they're *family!*

Joe Webster (12)
Wilmington Grammar School for Boys

The Terminator

Don't look now, but the Terminator's back,
His mission, to eliminate you, run!
The chase begins, you verse him.
You can run, but you can't hide.

Don't look back, he's on your tail,
He'll catch you, fast
And he won't fail.

You prove him wrong and get away,
Still you run just to be safe,
You hear his voice in your head saying,
'I'll be back!'

Harry Fiske (11)
Wilmington Grammar School for Boys

A Day At The Beach

The sun proudly rising,
Its shadow hanging over,
The empty and forlorn beach,
With the waves lapping gently over the shoreline.
The seagulls crying out,
Against the quietness of the early morning.

The sun smiling down,
Towering majestically.
The busy beach full of chattering people,
Children excited, running and dashing about.
The breeze getting up,
Gently making the waves froth at the edge,
Before coming gently down on the midday sun.

The moon looks over an angry sea,
Waves tossing and turning,
Crashing loudly over the sand.
The wind lashing and whistling on the deserted beach,
The buoys being bashed against the forceful waves.
Such a dark and stormy night!

Billy Ledger (12)
Wilmington Grammar School for Boys

Football (The Match Vs Portugal)

I like football, it's a game we play,
It's on TV, I'd watch it all day,
I'd play it all day but it's raining outside,
So I'll have to watch Becks hit it wide,
Then he misses and the crowd boo,
What can he do
Except see the groundsman
And threaten to sue?

Thomas Nankivell-Long (11)
Wilmington Grammar School for Boys

My Team, Gillingham

My team in their blue and white kit, storming down the pitch,
They're going for another goal, please not another hitch.
Playing the normal formation, the attacking 4-3-3,
Steve Banks is in goal, and great he may be,
But Jason Brown is defiantly the best to me.

I love the crowd, the stadium and the atmosphere,
While my dad sits down chanting, guzzling another beer.
Wait a while; we could come back to win,
As long as our defence does not go in the bin,
Iwan Roberts wins the game to relieve him of his sin.

The game ends, and I have a smile on my face,
Now we are in for the championship race.
Up against all the best,
This will be a real test,
But I think the lads need a rest.

Bradley Lonergan (11)
Wilmington Grammar School for Boys

The Man Who Died

When I walked down my street,
The mouse beneath my feet went squeak, squeak.
As I walked into my house,
My door went creak, creak.
As I walked up the stairs,
The floor beneath me went clonk, clonk.
When I was up the stairs,
A man appeared who stared and stared.
When he took his gun out,
The sound of the shot went bang, bang.
As I fell to the floor,
I could see no more, no more.

Martin Long (12)
Wilmington Grammar School for Boys

Autumn

Not many think that much of autumn,
As the summer is gone but winter is welcome.

The leaves are falling detached from the trees,
They blow to the ground and get caught up in the breeze.

The summer has gone and the good weather too,
Soon kids will complain with colds or with flu.

The leaves have changed colour, all yellow and red,
Kids don't go outside, they play in houses instead.

Colours fill the world with oranges and browns,
They fill up the villages, cities and towns.

After spring makes the plants, the summer helps grow them,
In the winter they die, so what about autumn.

In autumn great colours have painted the trees,
With less flowers you'll see less wasps and less bees.

So before you judge autumn just like many would,
You need to see further than the bad, like all of us should.

Ben Wilkinson (14)
Wilmington Grammar School for Boys

Christmas Time

Christmas is a time of sharing,
Wrapping paper ripped off
Here the people are caring,
People's frowns fall off,
Sitting round the fire,
Bringing joy to all,
Christmas tree for hire,
Reindeer flying all around.

George Read (11)
Wilmington Grammar School for Boys

Silent, Lonely Night

Silent, lonely night, oh how did it come?
Silent, lonely night, make a beeline for the gun.
Silent, lonely night, tear in her eye,
Silent, lonely night, what a time to die.
Silent, lonely night, fear in the air,
Silent, lonely night, who's gonna care?
Silent, lonely night, death before me,
Silent, lonely night, I must leave and flee.
Silent, lonely night, blood on my face,
Silent, lonely night, this has put me in my place.
Silent, lonely night, what have I done?
Silent, lonely night, in my ear like a drum.
Silent, lonely night, swift like a feather,
Silent, lonely night, will this haunt me forever?

Louis Mesure (12)
Wilmington Grammar School for Boys

That Sunday Morning

I woke up that Sunday morning,
What could I hear? It was Santa calling,
Just look at all that snow, there it lay,
Of course it was because it's Christmas Day.

Look at all that snow, it's time for a fight,
We can go on, all through the night.
This will be great and most fantastic,
This will be brilliant, I feel ecstatic.

Look at that beautiful Christmas tree,
And all those presents, they must be for me!
To end this poem, I will say,
This is the great life, Christmas Day.

Harry Stevens (11)
Wilmington Grammar School for Boys

My Family

My family owns a house
That is never as quiet as a mouse
My sisters are older than me
But boy, are they not funny

They boss me about
And often they shout
My mum's quite cool
My dad acts the fool

My cats are the best
But bring in the pests
My mum often shouts
To take them back out

Our house is quite small
Which makes me seem tall
Our garden is wide
With a gap up the side

It also has trees
Which scrape up my knees
And bushes of holly
Without any lolly

We have a large car
Which takes us quite far
But often we walk
Because it's easier to talk.

David Jacques (11)
Wilmington Grammar School for Boys

Rooney

There was a young boy named Rooney
Who liked to do a mooney
He showed his bum
Off to his mum
Then everyone called him Looney.

Gregory Martin (11)
Wilmington Grammar School for Boys

Miss Maple

Miss Maple, Miss Maple,
I need another staple.
Miss Maple, Miss Maple,
Tom's rocking the table.
Miss Maple, Miss Maple,
On my homework, what do you make?
How much longer until my morning break?

Miss Maple, Miss Maple,
Tom was hitting me.
Jason, Jason,
Wait dear, I'm drinking my tea.

Miss Maple, Miss Maple,
I need another staple.
Miss Maple, Miss Maple,
Tom's rocking the table.
Miss Maple, Miss Maple,
I've lost that pen of mine,
How much longer until lunchtime.

Miss Maple, Miss Maple,
Tom has stolen the art bibs.
Jason, Jason,
Please just stop telling fibs.

Miss Maple, Miss Maple,
I need another staple.
Miss Maple, Miss Maple,
Tom's rocking the table.
Miss Maple, Miss Maple,
I've ripped my sleeve,
How much longer until I can leave.

Joshua Madge
Wilmington Grammar School for Boys

Shredder

S hred, chew, swallow
H ollow are the trees in the deep, dark wood
R ed with blood are the teeth of the shredder
E ating always, even in the worst weather
D ying, dying
D evoured are its victims
E ek! Crunch! All these noises are making me shake
R un! Shredder the beast is wide awake.

Mounir Ingle (11)
Wilmington Grammar School for Boys

Arsenal

A is for *Arsenal,* the best team in the world
R is for *reigning,* all the best teams
S is for *shooting,* and scoring loads of goals
E is for *ever,* being the best team
N is for *nine,* scoring nine goals
A is for *agility,* the fastest team around
L is for *laughing,* at all the other teams.

George McCarthy (11)
Wilmington Grammar School for Boys

School

S is for scary, the teachers make me cry,
C is for caring, is that a lie?
H is for headmaster, he's horrible to me,
O is for oblivious. Who pays attention to me?
O is for observant, the teacher's big green eyes,
L is for lessons, we are taught in a large size.

Jordan Godwin (13)
Wilmington Grammar School for Boys

The Autumn Leaves Are Falling

T he autumn leaves are falling,
H ard against the earth,
E very leaf has turned to crispy brown.

A nd summer is a fading memory,
U nderneath the trees a golden carpet lays,
T he earth is damp and cold,
U p above and in the trees the birds are almost gone,
M igrating to far off lands,
N ight falls quickly.

L ight comes slowly,
E mpty from children playing are the streets,
A round the parks the echo of laughter is no more,
V ery still is everywhere,
E ndless it seems this time of year,
S uddenly the lights go on.

A nd the darkness is filled with life,
R eady soon for Christmas,
E veryone is lifted, children play and laugh.

F ather Christmas,
A ll that turkey!
L aughing,
L oving,
I dyllic,
N eeding,
G iving.

Luke Driscoll-Froggatt (11)
Wilmington Grammar School for Boys

Devil Poem

I was a good boy, but then I turned bad,
My teacher thought I was going mad,
I pulled out a shot gun and yelled shut up.

I blasted my teacher with a shot,
And by then I was feeling very hot,
She laid there screaming asking for healing.

My friends were amazed to what I had done,
And with that I sat down and ate a bun,
But as I didn't really care, my friends just stood in despair.

The head came to see about all the fuss,
He ran straight over to Miss Russ,
He went and sat down with Miss and said, *'Who did this?'*

I raised my hand and said it was me,
I said, 'Don't worry, it's only her knee.'
I walked out the room and didn't look back following my terrible attack.

I walked along the corridor smirking and smiling,
I tripped over and whacked my head,
And then I woke up and found I was in bed!

Matthew Gutteridge (12)
Wilmington Grammar School for Boys

Past

When you're small and growing up
It's hard to see the past
Life rushes past your eyes so quick
It happens very fast.

So here is something to remind you
Of the younger days . . .
Just think how long you'd last
If you talked a while with someone
From the good times of your past . . .

Joseph McMorrow (12)
Wilmington Grammar School for Boys

San Francisco

Holiday time has come at last,
Days of work at school have passed.
My trip to America is in sight,
Will I be able to sleep tonight?

We are flying on Virgin Airline,
Will the window seat be mine?
Taking off was such a *blast,*
San Francisco, here we come at last.

Touching down I saw the city,
The skyline dramatic, but also pretty.
Cable cars and trams to ride,
A bay to cross from side to side.

The world known Golden Gate Bridge,
It stands from ridge to ridge.
Alcatraz is surrounded by sea,
Isolated, deserted and very lonely.

Fisherman's Wharf and Pier 39,
Come here to see seals bask in the sunshine.
Clam chowder for sale on every street,
Seafood is what everyone likes to eat.

A crooked road called Lombard Street,
Cars wind their way at a slow speed.
Bells on cable cars chime and clang,
It all went past us in a bang.

Our days here are over, time to move on,
Pack up our cases, so sad to be gone.
San Francisco was great, but it's time to go,
Tomorrow we'll be in Lake Tahoe!

Robert Graham (11)
Wilmington Grammar School for Boys

Funeral Blues

Stop all the cars from moving,
Prevent the church bell from ringing,
Silence the children playing in the playground,
Bring out the coffin, let the mourners come.

Let helicopters hover above,
Moaning he is dead,
Put black armbands around the football players,
Let the world mourn this death.

He was my universe,
My Earth, Mars and Jupiter,
My night and day,
I thought that love would last forever; I was wrong.

The planets are not wanted now,
Pack up Mars and Jupiter even Earth,
Pour away the ocean,
For nothing now can ever come to any good.

Adam Green (12)
Wilmington Grammar School for Boys

In War

In war, you hear the screeching bullets,
Soldiers are surviving,
The bullets are biting,
The cannons are blasting,
Buildings turned to smithereens,
Snipers hiding, waiting,
Tanks blowing, firing,
There is cannon fodder,
Terrain turning red, blood,
People fleeing,
Victory,
But at a cost.

Andrew Dunmall (12)
Wilmington Grammar School for Boys

Dolphin

I wish I were under the sea,
A dolphin I would be,
I would go around anywhere,
But I wouldn't see a bear,
That is what I wish for.

Going round eating fish,
That makes a great dish,
Where do I go?
Hopefully there will be no snow,
That is what I wish for.

What is that noise?
Oh, it is those boys,
Swimming, jumping and taking a breath,
It feels like you're going deaf,
That is what I wish for.

I am feeling so ill,
I think it was that eel,
I am feeling so worn-out,
That is what you get for moving around,
You wouldn't believe it was a dream.

Charles Guenigault (12)
Wilmington Grammar School for Boys

What I Saw . . .

I saw a person upside down
Wearing a big, thick dressing gown.
I saw a brick up in the sky
As I looked up it hit my eye.
I saw a spider big and brown
I really hope it doesn't drown
In the bath of tumbling foam
Hurry spider get back home!

Charles Hutchins (11)
Wilmington Grammar School for Boys

Macbeth

Trouble maker,
Life taker.
Power seeker,
Crafty schemer.
Throne snatcher,
Soul catcher.
Letter reader,
Ambitions dreamer.
Norwegian defeater,
Night creeper,
King killer,
Country thriller.
Norwegian slayer,
Great betrayer.

Parlad Dahele (12)
Wilmington Grammar School for Boys

At The Water's Edge

At the water's edge,
The soft, calm sea,
The gentle breeze,
The warm air.

The sun shines brightly,
As yellow as butter,
Melting all my troubles away.

The sand,
So light and elegant,
The water, warm, shining,
At the water's edge.

Gopal Johal (12)
Wilmington Grammar School for Boys

What Is Life?

What is life about, work and play?
Is it only mobile phones to what happens every day?
Texting, voicemail, what about it?
These 'fashionable' things are killing us bit by bit.

Will work and play have its say?
Will these get us through the day?
Football, with this high spirit,
Will they get an alarmingly obese world fit?

Every day we go to school,
Someday everyone makes himself a fool.
Lessons, lessons, lessons, homework,
Is this what we do as 'work'?

Do we have to work and play?
Will these get us through the day?
School is sometimes boring,
When parents also sometimes adore.

Will work and play have its say?
Will these get us through the day?
Life, life, life,
Why is this life filled with so much strife?

Michael Littlemore (12)
Wilmington Grammar School for Boys

Destiny

What is your destiny? Will you live till you're 90,
Or will you die of a dreaded disease?

Will the doctors save your life or will it be too late?

Will you get treatment or will you refuse? I want you to remember,
Just think, today, will it be you tomorrow?

Does God decide when it's your time to go or is it up to you?
Was it decided when you were born or was it decided before?

Just wait and then you will know your fate.

Jacob Cann (11)
Wilmington Grammar School for Boys

Months Of The Year

January, here we come!
It's New Year's Day
There's lots of fun.

February's already here,
It's really cold
At this time of year.

March is windy, it's half-term,
Schools are out,
No need to learn.

It's April time, Easter's near,
Jesus died for us,
Then came back here.

May blows in, it's the end of spring,
In comes summer,
Let's see what it will bring.

It's June time now, there are fêtes and fairs,
There are plenty of stalls
All selling their wears.

July joy, it's the summer holiday,
When time is endless,
To sleep, rest and play.

August hot and sticky too,
Barbecues out
And the sky is blue.

September's getting a little bland,
Leaves are falling
On the farmer's land.

October's end mean Hallowe'en,
Trick or treat,
Run and scream.

November is full of light,
It smells of smoke
On bonfire night.,

December's here, it's the twenty-fifth,
Open your stocking,
To feel the bliss.

Lewis Baker-James (11)
Wilmington Grammar School for Boys

Autumn

A
leaf is
so quiet
when it falls. It
falls unexpectedly as
not to make a sound. The colour
changes so rapidly from green to red
to brown and then to yellow. The tree is
now bare and has no cover to hide all the
exploited nudity of all the branches and all
that is to cover is the bark of the tree trunk.
Autumn is now here so shout it out with
joy. Don't worry about snowball
fights, leave that for winter.
Leaf fights are now in
and are just as
good. Autumn
is here, so
lap up
all the
wet
weather.

Lewis Everest (14)
Wilmington Grammar School for Boys

My Brother Is An Alien

M ysterious he always will be,
Y et normal he will never be.

B igger he grows, the bigger his nose,
R ather than eat food he throws it around.
O thers run away when he comes,
T he house needs extensions for his head.
H is spaceship he keeps in the yard,
E ars need unplugging I think,
R aces he always loses.

I nsane he always is,
S ane he will never be.

A n alien I think he is,
N ow dumb as well.

A n alien I think he still is,
L ittle although he is,
I think he's normal now.
E ven better he's nicer now,
N ever again will I call him an alien.

Zachariah Lloyd (12)
Wilmington Grammar School for Boys

Summertime

S un, sun, sun, I'm so happy
U rgh! Not the time for changing my sister's nappy
M essing around in the sun
M unching away at a burger and bun
E ating ice creams and chilling out
R unning around and playing about
T ime to relax and chill down
I 'm so happy, here comes a clown
M y dad has finally come out to play
E njoying a wonderful time I've had today.

Nathan Moseby (12)
Wilmington Grammar School for Boys

All About Autumn

A is for autumn, when the leaves fall off the trees,
L is for long branches, that the leaves dangle from,
L is for luminous orange, the colour of the leaves this season.

A is for avenues, full of bright autumn colours,
B is for beautiful, as I see the trees in the autumn sun,
O is for oak, the giant acorn tree,
U is for undying, the never ending generations of trees,
T is for trees of beautiful shape.

A is for ash, the grey bark tree,
U is for useful, fallen leaves make compost,
T is for tiring, when you have to clean the leaves from your garden,
U is for untidy, the arrangements of branches,
M is for misty mornings, cold and silent,
N is for next year, when the next autumn comes.

Daniel Myles (11)
Wilmington Grammar School for Boys

Wilmington

W is for work, the homework that is set,
I is for ill, the times that I get.
L is for length, the short time there is,
M is for moaning, it makes me fizz.
I is for image, I might get a scare,
N is for nasty, the older boys are there.
G is for geography, my favourite subject yet,
T is for teachers, the craziest I've met.
O is for organising, the stress it makes,
N is for negotiating, the time it takes.

Michael Waters (11)
Wilmington Grammar School for Boys

My Garden

The grass is green and beautiful,
It bends beneath my feet,
The birds are sitting in the trees,
Looking for food to eat.

The grass is green and beautiful,
The sun begins to shine,
The wind begins to blow about
The washing on the line.

The grass is green and beautiful,
The leaves begin to fall,
The birds are leaving thick and fast,
They hear migration call.

The grass is white and beautiful,
The snow has fallen deep,
Beneath the snowy blanket,
The green grass is asleep.

Alan Barry (12)
Wilmington Grammar School for Boys

Birthday

Birthdays are my favourite
Birthdays are the best
I like my birthday because I get to see my family

Birthdays are my favourite
Birthdays are the best
I like my birthday because I get to see my friends

Birthdays are my favourite
Birthdays are the best
I like my birthday because I get to see my mum and dad

Birthdays are my favourite
Birthdays are the best
I love having all the cards because they make me think of you.

Matthew Murrant (11)
Wilmington Grammar School for Boys

Bonfire Night

As bonfire night comes around
You can clearly hear the distant sound
Of exploding fireworks in the sky
As crowds of people watch them fly
Off shoot the rockets into the dark
Going off with a bang and a blinding spark
This is surely a night to remember
A beautiful night on the 5th of November

As the night goes on so does the show
As fireworks give off their amazing glow
And as they shatter and colours break free
People's faces light up with glee
As they stand and stare at a wonderful sight
The colours of the rainbow light up the sky
This is surely a night to remember
A glorious night on the 5th of November

As the show begins to come to an end
A final surprise is what they will send
As tremendous rockets hoot from the ground
And as it travels there is not even a sound
As anxious people wait for the boom
And the terrific colours to brighten the gloom
As it explodes the sky starts to glow
And a river of colour starts to flow
As the burning fires start to die out
People leave with a happy shout
This is surely a night to remember
A terrific night on the 5th of November.

Andrew Holder (13)
Wilmington Grammar School for Boys

School Dinners

You walk into the dinner hall, the noise erupts,
The slurping of drinks, the clanking of cups.
The crashing of plates,
The laughter of your mates.
But then the sound dies down,
The headmaster's in town.

Banana skins spread over the floor,
Watch your step, you'll slide out the door.
Carrots and peas spread all around,
They drop off the plate and onto the ground.
Spaghetti and pasta, it tastes so nice,
Just as good as meatballs and rice.

Lunch is the best moment of the day,
Well that's what I would probably say.
It starts at 12 and finishes at 1,
For desert I have a currant bun.
Then there's the thumping of the vending machines,
And the silly behaviour of the Year 13s.

Then the teacher parades around,
Starts complaining about the noisy sound.
She says, 'Keep the noise down, it's much too loud,'
She says this to the joking six form crowd.
Then the bell goes, let's go back to class,
Registration's about to begin, we better go fast.

James Longley (12)
Wilmington Grammar School for Boys

Collection Of Limericks

There is a boy called Mike
Who once fell off his bike
He landed in a river
And then began to shiver
And was chased away by a pike,

There was a young lad called Andy
Who thought he was very handy
He grabbed a hammer
And a spanner
And drank a lager shandy.

There was once a man called Dan
Who liked to be called 'the man'
He was such a saint
When he went for some paint
For his number one fan.

There once was a girl from Cork
Who tried to eat peas on a fork
They all rolled away
And her mother did say
'From now on we shall all eat pork.'

There was a young girl called Helen
Who liked to eat lots of melon
One day she fell ill
Off of her window sill
And is now in a hospital called Dwellin.

Andreas Cowling (12)
Wilmington Grammar School for Boys

My Former Class

In my former class there were 31 of us
Amber, Angelo, Clare and Katie swim
Gabby is the actress of the class
Charlie is her counterpart
Philip, Stuart and Jack run
They all have special talents
Ellie is the monkey of the class
Whilst Laura N is the mad cow
James, Thomas, Jon and Joe
Are really, *really* weird
Laura S is the gymnast
Very good is she
Robert is very strange
He goes to this school
Ben J is a footballer
Tanika and Lucy, the quiet ones
Olivia is the auburn haired one
Emily, Sophie and Becca her friends
Jessica and Vanessa the smart girls
Eleanor and Josie at Wilmington Girls
Coral and Aleesha the best of friends
And finally me!
Obviously the best in the class
The netball player and the swimmer

That was my old class
My comfortable old class.

Benjamin Hayward (11)
Wilmington Grammar School for Boys

Good Morning

The soft pillow was against my hot cheek
The covers pulled over my head
As my dad said, 'Get up, it's the beginning of the school week'
I was awoken from my bed.

Daniel Davis (11)
Wilmington Grammar School for Boys

For This Is The Night To Remember

New Year's Eve is here,
Fire crackers appear,
The night gets darker,
My mind's a marker,
I'll remember this night for years.

It's my vision,
My big soul mission,
To create a miracle tonight,
For this is the night,
I'll show my might.

I'll prove my point,
I'll show I'm right,
For this is the night to remember.

The song books are out,
And so am I,
So I've raided the savings,
And left for Hastings.

The party was great,
And so was I,
So we grab the beer,
And finish the year.

Ben Hooper (13)
Wilmington Grammar School for Boys

Snowball

I made a little snowball,
As round as round could be,
I thought I'd keep it as a pet,
To sleep in bed with me.

I made it small pyjamas,
A night-cap for its head,
But then one day it ran away,
But first it wet the bed.

Matthew De La Pole (13)
Wilmington Grammar School for Boys

Air Guitar Land

Done sound check
All ready with my guitar
Dressed right
Hear the screaming of the crowd
Reading banners
'We love Tim!'
And seeing everyone waving
I'm on.

About to strike my guitar
Enter my best friend
'Tim, what on earth are you doing?'
Embarrassment
He found me, tennis racquet in hand
Hairbrush hanging from my bed
I was in 'Air guitar land'.

Tim Atkins (12)
Wilmington Grammar School for Boys

I Do Like - I Don't Like

I like football,
I like golf,
I like all sports
And other stuff.

I don't like homework,
I don't like school,
I don't like vegetable
And that's about all.

I like some things,
I don't like other things,
But I try to be happy
Whatever things I do!

Jack Murray (12)
Wilmington Grammar School for Boys

My Family

My family is a family of six,
Its members are a mix,
Some are sweet,
And nice to meet,
The others are a mean bunch,
They'd like to give you a punch.

There is Ellie, Sam and Aiden,
They used to play for Haden,
Next are Mum and Dad,
We aren't that bad,
Oh and there's me,
We're really nice you see.

We have fun,
In the sun,
We play around,
And fall on the ground,
We stick together,
Whatever the weather.

Murray Hibbard (12)
Wilmington Grammar School for Boys

The Life Of A Window

I cannot move, I cannot speak,
I stay here waiting, week by week.

I sit here in my rotting frame,
Watching people's lives, like a game.

Humans come, humans go,
Coming and going, to and fro.

Everybody looks right through me,
They don't even care, you see?

Christopher Coales (11)
Wilmington Grammar School for Boys

The Great Green Hippo

The great green hippo
Is very obese,
He's as big as Cindy,
She's my niece.

The great green hippo
Is oddly very green,
And I think it's the colour
That makes him so mean.

The great green hippo
Ate my friend Dan,
So with a massive great *bang*
He was dead.

Now I'm going to my grandad's
To thank him for the gun
That his dad gave him
From World War I.

Jack Hullett (12)
Wilmington Grammar School for Boys

Time

Time ticks endlessly
Tick, tick, tick
It's all around us every day
It seems it's fast when you play.

Time ticks endlessly
Tick, tick, tick
It's 24 hours night and day
As time ticks away.

Time ticks endlessly
Tick, tick, tick
Time ticks away, away
But we're not all here to stay.

Jak Halpin (11)
Wilmington Grammar School for Boys

Homework!

Doom and gloom
Shut in my room.

Homework . . .
It's a nightmare
It's not fair.

Homework . . .
It makes me despair
I don't care.

Homework . . .
It's a waste of time
And I can't rhyme.

Homework . . .
Practise makes perfect
I'm sure it'll be worth it.

Homework . . .
It makes you bright
If you do things right.

Homework . . .
The secret to succeed
You have to *read*.

Anthony Lavelle (11)
Wilmington Grammar School for Boys

Autumn

Winter, spring, summer
Autumn leaves fall to the floor
Cold winds blow around
The rain falls from the grey sky
The many colours
Brown, green, yellow, orange, grey
Harsh winter, cold air
Misty breath floats from your mouth.

Sacha Childs-Clarke (13)
Wilmington Grammar School for Boys

Football

F is for football, the best sport around
O is for oh no, we lost again
O is for oh yeah, I am a hat-trick hero
T is for team, they play on the pitch
B is for buying players to make a team better
A is for all of the team working together
L is for leagues, the things that teams play in
L is for lob, when you kick the ball over the keeper.

Chris Lock (11)
Wilmington Grammar School for Boys

Football

F is for dirty foul being made into a red card.
O is for an own goal made by a player's first touch.
O is for Michael Owen never scoring any goals.
T is for a triumphant victory over any team.
B is for a ball being hit into the crowd.
A is for a player being hacked.
L is for leaning messed up penalty spot.
L is for a lunged tackle into a defender.
   Millwall.

Ben Hodges (12)
Wilmington Grammar School for Boys

Winter

W indows frosted by the cold.
I diotic snowball fights.
N ights get longer and darker.
T errible cold, chattering teeth.
E at nice hot dinners after a cold day out.
R esting in front of the hot, burning fire,
   That's what winter means to me.

Steve Hirst (12)
Wilmington Grammar School for Boys

Football Hooligans

F ootball is the best sport,
O r at least I think.
O rdinary balls are size 5,
T he time of a game is 90 minutes.
B alls start flying around,
A nd people start booing and cheering.
L ittle people fish around for money,
L ittle moles make holes in the pitch.

H ooligans throw lighters at refs,
O i, how much are they paying you?
O n the ball is Joe Cole,
L ivers are aching,
I am sweating bad,
G eeks hate this wonderful game,
A nd people should respect footballers,
N ot disrespect them.
S o if you don't support West Ham, *be quiet!*

Ben Martin (12)
Wilmington Grammar School for Boys

Football

F is for foot that scores most of the goals
O is for offside, when a player runs in front of a defender
O is for own goal, when a player turns the ball in his own net
T is for throw-in when the ball has gone off
B is for ball that ends up in the goal
A is for atmosphere, what you get when the crowd is cheering
L is for legends like Ian Wright and Pele
L is for love, like I love football.

Jake Coppin (11)
Wilmington Grammar School for Boys

A Flower

You may think a flower is not that important,
But that is a lie, it is a symbol of *peace*.
When you are near them you feel at rest,
You sit there still watching a bird's nest.

A flower is a wonderful plant,
Some people look at them all day.
It gives people a boost of hope,
It feels better than smoking dope.

I like to look at a flower,
It makes me feel wonderful,
I prefer it to KFC,
It makes me chuckle, he he he.

A flower makes me happy,
It brings back good memories,
I want to watch it all day,
But I want to play, so hey.

Jonathan Dudley (12)
Wilmington Grammar School for Boys

Autumn

Weather getting colder and wetter,
Rain and fog everywhere,
Winds blowing to and fro,
Trees are empty, leaves turning brown and falling to the ground,
Everyone reaching for their hats and scarves.

Conkers growing on horse chestnut trees,
Experiencing shorter days,
Days gradually getting darker,
Animals are getting ready for hibernation.

Lewis McKenzie (13)
Wilmington Grammar School for Boys

I Remember

I remember, I remember, Mrs Corcoran's class in year R,
Meeting new friends, playing with toy cars.

I remember, I remember, Miss Pethig's class in Year 1,
Playing in the sandpit, that was fun.

I remember, I remember, Miss Pethig's class in Year 2,
Going on holiday, I bet my teacher would come too.

I remember, I remember, Mrs Wallis' class in Year 3,
Miss Wild brought in her chinchilla for everyone to see.

I remember, I remember, Miss Larington's class in Year 4,
Miss Larington read many books to us, The Famous Five and more.

I remember, I remember, Mrs Wallis' class in Year 5,
Playing with my best mates, Tom, Jack, Ashley, Nathan and Luke
make five!

I remember, I remember, Mrs Morgan's class in Year 6,
The 11+ was hard, but I got eighty-eight ticks.

Now I'm a Year 7 I'll have to say goodbye,
I'll move on to my next school and remember the good times.

Craig Chatfield (12)
Wilmington Grammar School for Boys

Old Mr McNowing

Old Mr McNowing
Would walk two blocks before he streaked.
Oh why, oh why would he do such a thing even at wedding.
He thought he was hip even though his bedtime was 7,
With words like groovy, he cost his son his first date,
He was locked in the basement.
So think about what you say, or you'll be in the basement.

PS: Stay away from retro.

Jamie Murphy (11)
Wilmington Grammar School for Boys

The Ghost Ship

There once was a magnificent ship that set sail,
It now lays at the bottom of the ocean, its body weak and frail.

The ship and crew never came to bay,
For it is still rotting on the sea floor to this very day.

The people on the ship did not have a chance,
it was the middle of the sea they hit the rock,
The vessel remains forever in its cold, watery dock.

The captain cost them their lives, he was drunk at the wheel,
But it doesn't matter anymore because there is nothing they feel.

The ship was leaking water in torrents,
It now sleeps with the seaweed, which is drifting in the current.

When the ship was hit it sank slowly into the gloom,
There it rests silently in its briny tomb.

Jack Ambrose (11)
Wilmington Grammar School for Boys

My Friend Harry

My friend Harry is in a world of his own,
Trapped in his own silly madness.
He seems to repeat everything you say,
Even though I don't know why.
I suggest you don't go and talk to him,
He'll say something stupid, like,
'Cat on a hot tin roof,'
Even through it's a movie and book.
It seems to be his favourite words.
All in all he's still my weird little friend,
Even if you don't think he's funny.
You'll be surprised how he makes you laugh,
When he says one stupid single *word!*

Lawrence Colgan (11)
Wilmington Grammar School for Boys

Florida

The sunshine state
The sea, the sand, all around
Universal, Disney are still to be found
The air is clear and fresh
Which will clear your spotty flesh
The rides are a thrill
The drinks and ice cream are made to chill
The food is really nice
Like Chinese oriental rice
The swimming pool is cool
Only if you go to the local shopping mall
The weather is fine
Like their continentally grown wine
MGM, Disney and Seaworld will make you scream
Universal, Busch Gardens and Island of Adventure will make
your eyes gleam
The people are kind
As you will find.

Beau Britton (13) & Sam Watts (12)
Wilmington Grammar School for Boys

My Brother

My brother sounds like a heaving rhinoceros when he breathes.
My brother sounds like an elephant stampeding in the desert
when he runs up the stairs.
My brother looks like a little Mexican bandit.
My brother feels soft to the touch when my fist hits his belly.
My brother feels like steel when he hits me back.
My brother smells like rotten veg when he pops.
My brother smells altogether.
My brother, after all his faults, makes me laugh and I wouldn't want
another.

Dean Moore (11)
Wilmington Grammar School for Boys

Hot Holidays

H ot, humid days, it's hard to breathe,
O n some days you just want to leave,
L ying in the sun soaking up the rays,
I deally you want to laze,
D olphins jump through the water,
A stonished as we're only in Malta,
Y es it's time to go and pack,
S hame we're having to go back.

Brad Allen (12)
Wilmington Grammar School for Boys

Autumn

A nother autumn half term holiday is here.
U ncertain of the weather we need to find our coats.
T ime to collect conkers, fallen apples and acorns.
U nder our feet as we play are the crispy brown leaves.
M y friend and I play Hallowe'en tricks.
N ights drawn in and soon fireworks will light up the night sky.

Sam Hartley (13)
Wilmington Grammar School for Boys

Autumn

A is amber, the colour of some leaves when they fall off the trees.
U is for up, up high the trees grow,
T is for trunk, the trunk of the tree,
U is for under, underground the roots grow for metres.
M is for misty, some days in autumn are cold and misty.
N is for nights, in autumn the nights draw in.

Elliott Cox (13)
Wilmington Grammar School for Boys

Mauritius

M y favourite place to be,
A way from all the factories,
U nder the sea you see colourful fish and coral
R aging hot weather through the year
I n the Indian Ocean
T iny fish come to your feet
I sland of heat and golden sand
U nlimited sun and blue skies
S ensational all the time!

Jake Clements (12)
Wilmington Grammar School for Boys

Hallowe'en

H is for horror, out in the night,
A is for apple bobbing, happening around us,
L is for loony night's sky
L is for less candy than others,
O is for October, the month it's in,
W is for witches on their broomsticks,
E is for evil in the night,
E is for candy shaped like eyes,
N is for night creatures which now come out.

Billy Cox (12)
Wilmington Grammar School for Boys

Karate

K is for kicks, which is better than fighting sticks.
A is for amazing, the quick moves of a grand master.
R is for rules, which are there to be obeyed.
A is for agility, the bendy body of the black belt.
T is for temper, which must be controlled.
E is for energy, the fitness of a true fighter.

Ben Coward (11)
Wilmington Grammar School for Boys

World War

The war goes on deep into the night,
All I can do is stay and fight.
For the night is dark but I know ahead,
That grass is covered in a bloody red.

And like a roaring wave death has come,
And I try and try and try to run.
But as I go I trip and see,
The true horror of war staring back at me.

Friends lie in need by my side,
Nowhere to go, nowhere to hide.
A cry of anguish, a cry of pain,
Over and over and over again.

The war goes on deep into the night,
My heart stops beating, no more can I fight.
This futile battle in which I fell,
But still soldiers must carry on in this living hell . . .

Nicholas Avramoussis (12)
Wilmington Grammar School for Boys

Poetry In General

Why is poetry so hard?
I find it really unfair.
I try and try, I really do,
But often I don't care.

Don't even bother trying,
Because I really won't change my mind.
Poetry started it 'cause
Poetry, to me, isn't kind.

Poetry is such a hard subject,
Looks like I'm never going to get it,
But personally, in my opinion,
Poetry is . . . bad.

Oliver Chandler (12)
Wilmington Grammar School for Boys

Round The World Limericks

There was a man from France,
Who did a very strange dance.
He slipped on the floor
And got an extremely large sore,
You'd say he was mad at first glance.

There was a girl from Crete,
Who had extremely large feet.
When she was seven
They were size eleven,
And people say they're sweet.

There was a boy from Spain,
Who always wore a thick chain.
One day he wore one as big,
And heavy as a pig,
In the end he died of pain.

Alex Humphris & Andrew Yacoub (12)
Wilmington Grammar School for Boys

Along The River

All along the river bank
Through the reeds tall
All the mums are chatting
While the babies brawl

Where the river is deepest
Where the bank is steepest
All the ducks quack
While the mums sit and chat

The babies love to play
On such a fine day.

Matthew Boyd (12)
Wilmington Grammar School for Boys

All The Changes That Autumn Has Created

Children playing in the cold and breezy wind,
swamped in their coats and hats.
Soon their cheeks are as red as a rose
and their noses really sore.
They come in to the nice warm house
Where it is all nice and warm.
All the changes that autumn has created
now its time has arrived.
Leaves are falling from the trees,
spinning around like a Catherine wheel
on a dark and gloomy November's night.
They make a crunchy and crumbly noise like a crisp
as they get trodden on as people stroll through them.
The sound is so gentle it could put a baby to sleep.
They are as ginger as a ginger cake
that has just been baked.
The yellowness is a yellow as a rising sun in the morning.
Workers are hard at work raking the gardens and fields
of the leaves that have fallen from the trees.
All the changes that autumn has created
now its time has arrived.

Jack Short (11)
Wilmington Grammar School for Boys

Christmas

Christmas is a white snowflake falling to the ground
Christmas is Jesus being born on this blessed day
Christmas is giving presents to one another
Christmas is about caring for each other
Christmas is eating turkey as a traditional feast
Christmas is a day to thank God for his wonderful creation
    Christmas is the *best!*

Mark Bell (11)
Wilmington Grammar School for Boys

Autumn

The leaves are falling, golden and brown,
The paths are covered in a crunchy and rough layer,
People wrap up to keep warm and snug,
And many stay inside and watch the leaves fall like raindrops.

As we step on the leaves on the path,
The leaves are perished and fly away,
Hurricanes of leaves are twisting and turning on the edge of the path,
And as we walk through them, leaves land gently in our hair.

A brisk wind blows our hair backwards
And the leaves are forced out of their newly made home,
And are forced to go and find a new home,
But they might not, and they may be forced to live on the ground,
Where it's wet and damp.

The grass in the fields is no longer green,
It has been injected with many other colours,
Which in many ways makes the fields more attractive to look at,
And makes them much easier to lie on,
Because the leaves are much drier than the grass.

The cold and stiffening wind blows on our faces,
And our cheeks turn raw and red, and turn the colour of cherries,
Which substitute for there being none in this season of resting.

This is also a season for solitude,
Almost all the streets are silent,
And all the animals that were scurrying around for food in the summer
Are now all asleep, and never make a sound.

But is this the season for celebrating,
Or is it the season for mourning our losses?
For the trees, it would be the season for mourning for
The loss of their leaves,
But it would also be the season for celebrating,
Because for trees, autumn is like the new year,
A chance to get their leaves back and
To do their purpose on Earth even better than last year!

Christopher Mills (12)
Wilmington Grammar School for Boys

It's Me

Beneath my skull I've got a creature,
Which can eat me away inside.
It spreads a disease
And infects my happiness.
It gives me beauty,
It gives me wisdom,
It gives me all I need.
It puts up a fight,
Locks up my feelings
And lets them slip out.
It's treated as royalty,
Gives out respect,
It receives pain,
It's a human being,
It's in my flesh.
It's me.

Alex Bee (11)
Wilmington Grammar School for Boys

In A Bunker

In a bunker all alone,
Everyone around you dead.
In a bunker all alone,
Family and friends at home in bed.
In a bunker all alone,
Checking no enemies are near.
In a bunker all alone,
Nights and days filled with fear.
In a bunker all alone,
Crying yourself to sleep every night.
In a bunker all alone,
Knowing next morning you'll have to fight.
In a bunker all alone,
Gun in your hand ready and alert.
In a bunker all alone.

Jack Smith (12)
Wilmington Grammar School for Boys

The Sub

Silence was all around us,
As we slowly drifted to sea.
I had no idea
Of what awaited me.

The radar beeped,
Into action we shot.
The engines roaring,
Fear we had not.

We watched the screen,
Holding our heads up high,
We were not frightened,
Not afraid to die!

The sea was our home,
And we knew too well,
From the time we were born
To the time we rang that very last bell.

We said our prayers
Standing hand in hand.
Would we ever again
See our homeland?

James Chandler (12)
Wilmington Grammar School for Boys

Help Me

H is for help, I'm falling
E is for eagle attacking me
L is for lost, I've lost everything
P is for people who are below me

M is for mountain that I'm falling off
E is for eagle, it's rescuing me.

Jordan Saville (12)
Wilmington Grammar School for Boys

Helm's Deep

(Based on 'The Lord Of The Rings' by J R R Tolkien)

It is of Helm's Deep, of which I speak,
With a history grim and bleak,
There fell the Rohirrim fair
And the orcs from Orthanc, Saruman's evil lair.
With Rohan was Aragorn Eessar,
With bravery beyond compare,
With him was Legolas,
From the forest of old fairness.
By his side was Gimli with a dwarfish pride,
Who fought with an axe by his side.
At first the orcs attacked the Dike,
The defenders there took a hike,
Back to the Hornburg, the Rohirrim fled,
In their voices there was dread.
Saruman's army attacked the wall,
That was made of stone, proud and tall.
And when the orcs crawled through the grating like rats,
The men of Rohan cursed them well, 'Drat!'
But to the orcs' dismay,
Gimli, Gloin's son, stood in their way.
As he began to kill,
More and more orcs were added to the butcher's bill.
Up the orcs blew the wall with the delivery of Orthanc,
Like a shell shot from a mighty tank,
Then Aragorn spoke of dawn,
And out came Théoden, mowing down orcs like a mower on a lawn,
And through the breach came Mithrandir,
And the Eorlingas against the foe's rear,
Led by Ekenbrand,
Hammer of the White Hand.

Samuel Aylmer (12)
Wilmington Grammar School for Boys

Big Cats

There are four main types of big cat,
These do not lie on a mat.
First we have the lion, sleepy all day,
Including the month of May.
They also let the females hunt,
Unless they are a little runt.
Next we have the tiger, stripy they are,
You can't see them from afar.
They blend in well with the grass,
You can't see them even if you pass.
Now comes the cheetah, fast they can be,
They can run faster than even me.
They have an effective way to make animals die,
Especially if the prey's looking at the sky.
Finally there's the leopard, climb trees they do,
They look as if they will shout 'Boo!'
They bring their dinner up into the tree,
Although they get pestered by a bee.
There are other big cats,
That also do not lie on mats.
Here we have the lynx, with tufts on their ears,
They like to prey on deers.
Also there is the jaguar, lives in the jungle it does,
The leopard is his cuz.
Now there is the puma, smallest of the lot,
On the hillside it's just a minute dot.
There is also the snow leopard, covered in snow,
If they want to they can really go.
The last one is the black leopard, which is rare,
At night they will give you a scare.

Paul Cooper (12)
Wilmington Grammar School for Boys

Poem

H is for horrors terrorising streets
A is for aching teeth the next day
L is for lamp posts being attacked
L is for leprechauns locked up in cupboards
O is for old people getting scared
W is for witches flying on brooms
E' is for elephants trampling the streets
E is for experts hiding their stash
N is for no parking signs being vandalised.

Richard Butcher (12)
Wilmington Grammar School for Boys

Conflict

C is for conquering other countries, what happens in conflict.
O is for the opposition, who the fight is against.
N is for nocturnal, soldiers have to be this when on night watch.
F is for the flames, the result of bombing.
L is for the labour that is needed for repairs afterwards.
I is for indignant, your feelings towards the enemies.
C is for coward, there are none of these in conflict.
T is for terror, the feelings of innocent civilians.

Stuart Sardena (13)
Wilmington Grammar School for Boys

Autumn

A mazingly beautiful
U nreal colours
T hanksgiving tumbling in leaves
U ntimely leaves
M ajestical and magical
N ovember times are great.

Luke Brace (13)
Wilmington Grammar School for Boys

My School

W is for work all day into the night
I is for illness, it comes with a fright
L is for loud, everything and everyone
M is for madness, the homework we get done
I is for image, I feel like a teacher's pet
N is for nasty, most of the teachers I've met
G is for games, I wish and I hope
T is for teachers, they just can't cope
O is for organising, the horror it causes
N is for non-stop work without pauses

G is for God, please help us
R is running to catch the bus
A is for appearance, I hate wearing a tie
M is for more work, then I cry
M is for mess, so much I can't look
A is for amnesia, my excuse for forgetting my book
R is for revolting, the dinners we get.

Alec Bradley (11)
Wilmington Grammar School for Boys

Formula 1 Poem

F ormula 1, the fast and furious race,
O rientating the cars around the track,
R acing the wheel nuts off the cars and
M anoeuvring themselves through the traffic,
U ndoubtedly like magic,
L earning the tracks along the way,
A t speeds too fast to think of, racing for the ultimate prize!

1 *st place!*

Davie Young (12)
Wilmington Grammar School for Boys

The Dreaded Headmaster

The horrid break time bell rang out loud,
Ring, ring, ring!
The high-pitched loudness soon died down as the dreaded
                                        headmaster walked in.
Take one move or move one muscle, believe me you won't
                                        want to again.
As the Head has a terrible weapon that whips you now and then.

No one moved one bit, not even the geezer at the back,
But then the head bellowed out loud and said,
'Oi you, on your larry, sitting at the back, you blinked, now come
                                        over 'ere!'
The lad did as he was told, and did it fairly quick.

He stood up to the Head as bravely as he could,
We all stood there watching the torture that we heard,
'Pull down your underwear boy, this is gonna *hurt!*'
Some people closed their eyes, I watched in despair,
Crack! went the deadly weapon on his bottom bare,
'Owww!' the poor boy cried in fear.

The Head of course enjoyed the lot, but we did not,
The little lad could hardly walk, he crawled across the floor,
In fact he liked it so much that he sent us crawling home.

Scott Brown (11)
Wilmington Grammar School for Boys

Pencil Case

Around me are pens, pencils and rulers,
With them are sharpeners, rubbers and protractors,
I am an orange crayon in a big dark evil pencil case,
Compasses are nasty, they poke pens and pencils,
Rubbers are worse, they rub out our hard work,
I love neat, blue and beautiful ink pens,
But I'm a stupid messy crayon which babies use.

Harry Backhouse (11)
Wilmington Grammar School for Boys

The Premiership

T he most exciting league in the world
H ard tackles flying in from everywhere
E very player and manager, class and ready to win

P eople can't get tickets for matches
R aring to go and wanting to win
E ven the referees are class
M agic football takes place
I n every player's mind football exists
'E very player is so good, what team do I put out?' they say
    to themselves
R unning kills them physically
S ome of the football they play, people can't believe their eyes
H atred exists between each day; a derby begins
 I n games, fatigue levels are high,
P layers are on such big money.

George Carroll (12) & Charlie Cope (11)
Wilmington Grammar School for Boys

Summertime

S mell of flowers and fresh cut grass
U nder the shade while insects pass
M y feet are touching green blades beneath me
M iles and miles of blue sky, I see
E ating the burnt meat, that my dad cooked
R estaurants are what my mum had booked
T ime for bed, it's not over yet
I think there's one thing not to forget
M y poem has no wrong thing
E xcept for the fact that it's only spring!

Nicholas Hulls (12)
Wilmington Grammar School for Boys

The Planet

The land and sea,
It fills me with glee.
We call it a planet,
But I don't know who ran it.

It has a beautiful landscape,
And the humans on it are 99.9% like apes.
It is filled with different creatures,
Whom a lot are preachers.

From space,
It really does look ace.
It's fairly clean,
But there is a lot of litter to be seen.

The thinning ozone layer is harming our planet,
But it doesn't seem to bother us one bit.
I believe that the Earth will explode,
If we carry on down this road.

Robert Bennett (13)
Wilmington Grammar School for Boys

Fireworks

F lashing in the midnight sky,
I ndigo, blue, red and green,
R acing, darting, whooshing by,
E very colour can be seen,
W hirling, twirling Catherine wheel,
O ohs and aahs the crowd will cry,
R ainbow sky, a hot dog meal,
K eep well back when rockets fly.

Steven Rockingham (11)
Wilmington Grammar School for Boys

Monster In My Room

When my mum puts me to bed
And leaves me in the gloom,
I've always thought, don't ask me why,
There's a monster in my room.

It gets up, looks around,
And sniffs from left to right,
I never know and dare to think
When it's going to bite.

No one in my class hears monsters
They would have done at six,
And when I tell, about this beast
They beat me up with sticks.

My friends at school all say the same,
They think I'm going mad,
It's even worse with my sister's friends,
They all think I'm sad.

But if there was a monster
That really did kill me,
My friends, my mum and sister's friends
Would all be able to see.

That there was a monster in my room
That really did exist
They could check my corpse and see the blood
Where the monster bit my wrist.

Peter Brookes (12)
Wilmington Grammar School for Boys

Delightful Old Girl

Black with lumps
White brows 'n' chin
She is the queen of breakin' wind.
In the kitchen
On the stairs
She will do it anywhere.
In the corners she will sit
Having her daily shaking fit
All because of little things
That have six legs and a pair of wings.
Throwing cushions on the fire
Is one of her great desires
Many people say she's insane
It's not her fault she has no brain.
There's nothing that she won't eat
Cowpats, toe nails and mouldy meat.
Skidding across the dining room floor
A nice brown trail from door to door.
What she gets up to in the night
Will often give her owners a fright.
A big, fat puddle all over the floor
A nice white lab coat - not anymore.
Even though she's not too big
She'll always be our little black pig.

Morris Mitchener (12)
Wilmington Grammar School for Boys

Summer

S is for the sun
U is for us
M is for the morning
M is for merryful
E is for excited
R is for the rainbow.

Zac Burch (11)
Wilmington Grammar School for Boys

That Old Farm

That old farm that lies on the hill
As the days go by so does the farmer that owns it
As he cleans his tractor covered in grit
The farm on the hill is getting old like the farmer's mum
This makes the farm look glum
When he farms his vegetables he looks at the farm
And thinks of days gone by
His love for it, is like the love for another girl or guy
As the wind blows through his hair
When he retires, he will have no care for that old farm on the hill
He returns on his tractor, as he does, young punks throw things at him
Remembering the days when he was young and started crying
His tractor pulls up outside his house
He goes inside, his mum raises her hand, he cowers like a mouse
He walks into the living room
Where his mum grows mushrooms
So the farmer sits down
And listens to Darius
On the television
He is singing 'I'm Colour Blind'
The words are kept in his mind
And he goes to get a haircut as well
The sadness of his life grows stronger
And his life grows longer but shorter by the year
And so does his hair
These thoughts will stop
And so will this poem.

Mathew Ballard (11)
Wilmington Grammar School for Boys

Life

When I was born
I was just like a pawn,
Small and weak,
At risk and meek.

When I was 5
I was named Clive,
I liked the name,
It brought me fame.
(Within my family.)

When I was 10
My dad named Ken,
Told me life
Was full of strife.

When I was 15
I was really mean,
Mood swings drove me
Absolutely balmy.

When I was 20
I was very petty,
Life troubled me not,
I didn't think about a lot.

When I became 25
My life took a great, big dive,
I was sniffing glue and coke
And having 20 every day
(A smoke.)

Not one year later I met my end,
I drowned myself in a u-bend.
My life took an even bigger dive,
And that was the end of Clive.

Jonathan Keogh & Cyril Baptist (12)
Wilmington Grammar School for Boys